THE
MEDICAL
MISCELLANY

THE
MEDICAL
MISCELLANY

Conceived, designed, compiled, and written

by

Manoj Ramachandran and Max Ronson

Hammersmith Press
London, UK

First published in 2005 by Hammersmith Press Limited
Of 496 Fulham Palace Road, London SW6 6JD, UK

© Manoj Ramachandran & Jeffrey Aronson

British Library Cataloguing in Publication Data: A CIP record of this book is
available from the British Library.

ISBN 1-905140-05-3

Designed and typeset by Julie Delf
Commissioning editor: Georgina Bentliff
Production by Helen Whitehorn, Pathmedia
Cover illustration by Abby Franklin

Printed and bound by Replika Press, India

ABOUT THE AUTHORS

Manoj Ramachandran is currently an orthopaedic surgeon in London. His hobbies include obsessive bibliomania, random thought processes, and an unhealthy interest in the arts. He is available to speak incessantly.
manojorthopod@gmail.com

Max Ronson is a freelance layabout and compiler of crosswords.
mr@dr.org

THANKS AND BLAME

THE AUTHORS would like to thank the following for their help, inspiration, and suggestions (any errors in this book are entirely due to them):
Jeff Aronson, Judith Broomfield, Nicola Broomfield, Deborah Eastwood, Mike Fox, Richard Green, David Westwood, Amy Wilson, and the staff at the Wellcome and British Libraries.

MANOJ R would like to thank Navin Ramachandran, Puliakode Ramachandran, and Thankam Ramachandran. He reserves his deepest thanks though for Joanna - this book is her book too.

MAX R would like to thank his wife for constant emotional support and tea and cakes galore.

26 July: Manoj Ramachandran   31 June: Max Ronson

ACKNOWLEDGEMENTS

The extract from *Doctor in the House* by Richard Gordon is reproduced by permission of Curtis Brown Group Ltd © Richard Gordon 1952

The Environment and Disease: Association or Causation by Sir Austin Bradford Hill was first published in *The Proceedings of the Royal Society of Medicine*, 1965, volume 58, page 295 and is quoted here by permission from the Royal Society of Medicine.

The extract from *The Hitch Hiker's Guide to the Galaxy*, by Douglas Adams, 1979, is reproduced by permission from Pan Macmillan.

The poem *Cancer's a Funny Thing* by John Burdon Haldane is taken from an article that first appeared in the New Statesman in 1964 and is reproduced here with their permission.

The extract on Rectal Foreign Bodies by David B Busch and James R Starling is reprinted from *Surgery*, volume 100, Busch DB & Starling JR, Rectal Foreign Bodies: case report and a comprehensive review of the world's literature, pages 512-519, ©1986, with permission from Elsevier.

The extract on Rectal Foreign Bodies from *Bailey & Love's Short Practice of Surgery* (24th edition, edited by Russell, Williams & Bulstrode) is reprinted by permission of Edward Arnold.

The list under *Don'ts for Diagnosticians* was written by Sir Robert Hutchison and was first published in the *British Medical Journal*, 1928, volume 28, pages 335-337. It is reproduced in the Medical Miscellany with permission from the BMJ Publishing Group.

We have made every effort to obtain permission for the reproduction of any copyright material, but if you have any queries about this please contact us at http://www.hammersmithpress.co.uk

WE OFFER
A MEDICAL MISCELLANY
OR
CLINICAL CLAMJAMPHRIE

An Allopathic Assortment
A Bones's Balderdash
A Consultant's Companion
A Dental Diversity
An Empirical Embroilment
A Forensic Farrago
A Geriatric Gallimaufry
A Healthy Hotch-potch
An Iatrogenic Imbroglio
A Jurisprudential Jumble
A Klinical Kaleidoscope
A Leech's Lore
A Mountebank's Mishmash
A Nurses' Nincompoopery
An Orthopaedic Omnium-gatherum
A Paramedical Pot-pourri
A Quack's Quodlibet
A Registrar's Ragbag
An SHO's Salmagundi
A Therapeutic Thesaurus
Ultrasensual Utterances
A Venereologist's Vade mecum
A Wet-nurses' Witches' brew
An X-radiological Xenomania
A Yeasty Yakkety-yak
A Zoiatric Zoo

…with notable people's birth dates at the foot of each page

DOCTORS' DESIGNATIONS

Charlatans
Wont to prattle (Italian: ciarlare) about their medicines.

Bones or sawbones
That's what they do.

Leeches
They suck your blood.

Mountebanks
*Men who climbed on to a soapbox (Italian: monte banco) to shout
their wares at a fair.*

Quacks
*Originally called quacksalvers, supposedly because they "quacked""
or boasted about their salves.*

HANDEDNESS

How can you tell if someone is right-handed or left-handed? The muscles in
the dominant arm may be better developed; there may be more calluses on the
dominant hand, and in smokers, the fingers of the dominant hand may be
tar-stained, but not always. Colin Dexter does not tell us whether Inspector
Morse is right-handed or left-handed, but if the former, he may have his tar
stains on the left hand, since, besides being a smoker, he is a keen drinker and
cruciverbalist, and will use his right hand for those purposes, holding his
cigarette in his left hand.

CONDOMS AT RISK

Several everyday products can damage and therefore reduce the efficiency of
condoms and other latex products such as diaphragms. Those that are worth
noting include:

*Margarine   Butter   Low-fat spreads   Cream   Ice-cream
Salad oil   Baby oil   Petroleum jelly   Vaseline
Lipstick   Cooking oil   Suntan oil   Hair conditioners
Skin softeners   Massage oils*

---

4 January: Louis Braille (1809-52)
French educator and inventor of the Braille alphabet

ETYMOLOGY: SYPHILIS

Girolamo Fracastoro (1478-1553), a renowned physician, poet, and scholar from Verona in Italy, first coined the term "syphilis" in 1530, after the eponymous shepherd hero of his Latin hexameter poem of 1300 verses, entitled *Syphilis sive morbus Gallicus* (Syphilis, or the French disease). Fracastoro may have based Syphilis (often spelt Syphilus) on a medieval form of Sipylus, a son of Niobe in Ovid's *Metamorphoses*. During this era, as syphilis ravaged Europe, cause unknown, nations took turns in naming the disease after their enemies:

Le mal de Naples (France)	*The Italian disease (France)*
The Spanish disease (Italy)	*The French pox (England)*
The Canton disease (China)	*The Chinese disease (Japan)*
The Polish disease	*The English disease*

The French also named syphilis *la grosse verole* or "the great pox" to distinguish it from *la petite verole* or smallpox. It has also been suggested that chickenpox may be the very little pox, from the chickeen or chick, an Indian coin worth about four rupees. The cause of syphilis is now known to be the spirochaete bacterium *Treponema pallidum*. On July 17 1998, in *Science*, a renowned scientific journal, a research team of thirty-three co-authors revealed a schematic map of the bacterium's 1041 genes (comprising 1,138,006 base pairs), the number just falling short of the number of verses in Fracastoro's original poem.

FAMOUS SUFFERERS:
DEMENTIA

Enid Blyton   Charles Bronson   Winston Churchill   Perry Como
Ralph Waldo Emerson   Rita Hayworth
Charlton Heston   Burgess Meredith[1]   Iris Murdoch
Maurice Ravel   Ronald Reagan   Sugar Ray Robinson
Margaret Rutherford   E. B. White[2]   Harold Wilson

[1] American actor who played Rocky Balboa's trainer in the Rocky film series
[2] American author best known for children's books Stuart Little and Charlotte's Web

5 January: Joseph Erlanger (1874-1965)
Discovery of functions of neurons, Nobel prize 1944

ALLITERATIVE ABNORMALITIES

Digitalis dementia

Manganese madness

Myxoedematous madness

Fair, fat, female, fertile, and forty
(risk factors for gallstones)

Dermatitis, dementia, diarrhoea, and death
(the effects of pellagra, owing to nicotinamide deficiency)

THE AMINO ACID ALPHABET

A	Alanine	Alanine	A
C	Cysteine	Arginine	R
D	Aspartic acid	Asparagine	N
E	Glutamic acid	Aspartic acid	D
F	Phenylalanine	Cysteine	C
G	Glycine	Glutamic acid	E
H	Histidine	Glutamine	Q
I	Isoleucine	Glycine	G
K	Lysine	Histidine	H
L	Leucine	Isoleucine	I
M	Methionine	Leucine	L
N	Asparagine	Lysine	K
P	Proline	Methionine	M
Q	Glutamine	Phenylalanine	F
R	Arginine	Proline	P
S	Serine	Serine	S
T	Threonine	Threonine	T
V	Valine	Tryptophan	W
W	Tryptophan	Tyrosine	Y
Y	Tyrosine	Valine	V

The origin of the single-letter code for amino acids is attributed to Dr Margaret Oakley Dayhoff (1925-1983), founder of the field of bioinformatics. She shortened the code from their original three letter designations to the single letter code in an effort to reduce the size of the data files needed to describe the sequence of amino acids in a protein. Some of her shortened versions may be obvious but she clearly was running out of choices towards the end...

---

6 January: Percival Pott (1714-88)
English surgeon who described scrotal cancer in chimney sweeps

---

ALCHEMY

Alchemy, the scientific forerunner of chemistry, was the study of how base metals could be transmuted into gold (the word is from the Arabic *al-kimiya*, meaning transmutation). Alchemists, of whom the most famous was Paracelsus, sought the philosopher's stone, a universal solvent or alkahest, a universal remedy called a panacea, and an elixir of life. But if such a solvent existed, one might have difficulty finding a container in which to keep it.

George Ripley, in his treatise "The Compound of Alchemie" (1471), which he dedicated to Edward IV, described the twelve stages in the transmutation of the elements:

> *Calcination*
> *Dissolution*
> *Separation*
> *Conjunction*
> *Putrefaction*
> *Congelation*
> *Cibation*
> *Sublimation*
> *Fermentation*
> *Exaltation*
> *Multiplication*
> *Projection*

In his play *The Alchemist* (1610), Ben Jonson used the search for the philosopher's stone to satirize human gullibility and duplicity. Subtle, the alchemist, and his assistant, Dol Common, swindle Sir Epicure Mammon and others, whose cupidity and lechery leave them open to the blandishments of the rogues.

UNSCIENTIFIC NAMES: A-GO-GO

The full name of the HERG channel, a potassium channel, is the Human Ether-a-go-go Related Gene channel. Inhibition of the HERG channel in the heart changes the electrical potential and can therefore lead to abnormal rhythms. The most important arrhythmia that this causes is called *torsade de pointes*, which means twisting of the points, a term that is taken from ballet and refers to the change in the electrical axis of the heart.

---

9 January: Har Gobind Khorana (1922-)
Structure of nucleotides, Nobel prize 1968

THE ABC OF THE POLYPILL

The Polypill is a combination of six different medicines, which if taken together reduce the risk of cardiovascular disease (heart attacks and strokes) by over 80% (*BMJ* 2003; 326: 1419). The six ingredients are:

A: *Aspirin*   B: *Beta-blocker*
C: *Cholesterol-lowering statin*   D: *Diuretic (a thiazide)*
E: *Enzyme inhibitor (ACE inhibitor)*   F: *Folic acid*

MEDICS ON TV AND THE SILVER SCREEN

Dr Bethune (Donald Sutherland)
Dangerfield (Nigel le Vaillant)
Doogie Howser MD (Neil Patrick Harris)
Dr Doug Ross (ER) (George Clooney)
Dr Finlay (Dr Finlay's Casebook and Doctor Finlay)[1]
Hawkeye Pierce (M.A.S.H.) (Donald Sutherland)
Dr Kildare (Richard Chamberlain)[2]
Dr Kimble (The Fugitive)[3]
Dr Nick (The Simpsons)
Dr No (Joseph Wiseman)[4]
Quincy MD (Jack Klugman)
Dr Quinn, Medicine Woman (Jane Seymour)
Dr Socrates (Paul Muni)
Sir Lancelot Spratt[5]
Doctor Zhivago (Omar Sharif)

[1]Based on stories by A. J. Cronin; first played on TV by Bill Simpson and later by David Rintoul.
[2]Based on stories by Max Brand (Frederick Faust), who also wrote "Destry Rides Again" and other Westerns; played on the silver screen by Joel McCrea and Lew Ayres
[3]David Janssen on the small screen, Harrison Ford on the large
[4]The first James Bond film (1962) based on the novel (1958) by Ian Fleming, in which Julius No enrols himself in the Faculty of Medicine in Milwaukee, having survived shooting through the heart by hired killers, because he has dextrocardia (his heart is on the right side of his body).
[5]In *Doctor in the House* (1952) by Richard Gordon (Richard Gordon Ostlere); Sir Lancelot, chief surgeon at the fictional St Swithin's Hospital, "represented a generation of colourful, energetic surgeons that, like fulminating cases of scarlet fever, are rarely seen in hospital wards these days. He inherited the professional aggression of Liston, Paget, Percival Pott, and Moynihan." In the series of films based on Gordon's Doctor books, James Robertson Justice played Sir Lancelot with enormous gusto.

---

11 January: Roger Guillemin (1924-)
Identification of hypothalamic hormones, Nobel prize 1977

FAMOUS AMPUTEES

Real life	Fictional
Sir Douglas Bader	*Captain Ahab (Moby-Dick)*
Xavier Torres	*Captain Hook (Peter Pan & Wendy)*
Heather Mills-McCartney	*Professor Jordan (The 39 Steps)*
Horatio Lord Nelson	*Dr Robert "Rocket" Romano (ER)*
Peter Stuyvesant	*Luke Skywalker (The Empire Strikes Back)*

KEYHOLE SURGERY

The earliest example of keyhole surgery was the operation called keyhole iridectomy, a term that seems to have been coined in the late 1950s (see Johnson DS, Pino RH. Keyhole and peripheral iridectomies in different eyes in the same patient. *AMA Arch Ophthalmol* 1957; 58: 421-5). However, keyhole surgery as we know it today did not come into its own until the 1990s (see, for example, McCloy R. Through the keyhole. *Health Serv J* 1992; 102: 26-7).

But Richard Gordon seems to have been long ahead of the game. Here he is, writing in *Doctor in the House* (reproduced by permission of Curtis Brown Group Ltd., © Richard Gordon 1952):

> *"Where are we going to put the incision?" Sir Lancelot asked. By now the patient was forgotten; it was the lump we were after. Sir Lancelot had an upsetting habit of treating the owners of lumps as if they were already rendered unconscious by the anaesthetic.*
>
> *I drew a modest line over the incision.*
>
> *"Keyhole surgery!" said Sir Lancelot with contempt. "Damnable! Give me the pencil!" He snatched it away. "This, gentlemen, will be our incision."*
>
> *He drew a broad, decisive, red sweep from the patient's ribs to below his umbilicus.*
>
> *"We will open the patient like that. Then we can have a good look inside. It's no good rummaging around an abdomen if you can't get your hand in comfortably…"*

UNSCIENTIFIC NAMES: POPEYE

A gene family (popdc) encoding proteins in muscle cell membranes.

---

12 January: Paul Hermann Müller (1899-1965)
Discovery of DDT as an insecticide, Nobel prize 1948

RITES DE PASSAGE

The term *rites de passage* was first used, as the title of a 1909 book, by the Belgian anthropologist Arnold van Gennep, to describe the rituals that mark an individual's transition from one social status to another. The main rites are birth, puberty, first sexual experience, marriage, giving birth, divorce, menopause, retirement, and death.

Katherine Dunham's ballet *Rites de Passage*, first performed at the Curran Theatre in San Francisco in 1941, was in four parts – *Puberty* (initiation into manhood), *Fertility* (sexual experience), *Death*, and *Women's Mysteries* (puberty, menstruation, and giving birth).

William Golding's novel *Rites of Passage* (1980) is the first of a trilogy; the other two being *Close Quarters* (1987), and *Fire Down Below* (1989). The title refers to the coming of age of its main character, Edmund Talbot, to the death of another, the Reverend Colley, and to the rites that accompany the passage of a ship from England to Australia, such as crossing the equator.

COGNATE ANAGRAMS

A carotid artery	To carry heart tide
A morphine addict	Man hit acrid dope
Infantile paralysis	Is an early spinal fit
Masturbation	Rub, anatomist!
Medical consultations	Noted miscalculations
Night sweats	Waste things
Osteopath	He pats too
Roentgen's cathode rays	A stronger eye doth scan
Surgeon	Go nurse
Surgical instruments	Smart curing utensils
Surgical operation	Cure ail or stop gain
Therapeutics	Apt is the cure
The deadly nightshade	Thing had deathly seed
The dentist	Dints teeth
Deputy coroners	Tend your corpse
The medical profession	Find healers composite
The pharmacist	Ah! Part chemist (or Art chemist? Pah!)
The trained nurses	Tender hearts in us

---

14 January: Albert Schweitzer (1875-1965)
Humanitarian, theologian, missionary, organist, and medical doctor

The Grand Tour

It was customary in the 17th and 18th centuries for young men of good breeding to round off their education by making what was known as the Grand Tour, a tour of the major cities of Continental Europe, often in the company of a tutor or guide. Originally the grand tour (a rendition of the French *le grand tour*) referred only to France; the tour of Italy was known as the *giro*. But the term was subsequently extended to include any part of Europe (usually France and Italy) that the young man visited; Laurence Sterne's account of Parson Yorick's travels *A Sentimental Journey Through France and Italy* (1768) reflects this. The medical equivalent was a grand tour of the important continental schools of physic. Examples include:

Sir Thomas Browne (1605-1682), English physician and author, who spent three years in Paris, Montpellier, and Padua, graduating in Padua in 1633.

John Coakley Lettsom (1744-1815), English Quaker physician, who freed all the slaves on his father's Caribbean plantation and wrote extensively on poverty, prostitution, infectious illnesses, and penal reform; he toured Paris, Spa, Aix-la-Chapelle, and finally Leyden, where he graduated MD in 1769 with a dissertation on the virtues of drinking tea, entitled *Observationes ad vires theae pertinentes*.

William Withering (1741-1799), English physician and botanist, who in 1785 published *An Account of the Foxglove and some of its Medical Uses*, outlining the use of digitalis in cardiac disease, along with symptoms of toxicity; he started his tour in 1766 in Paris, but was forced to return prematurely when his companion, a Mr Townshend, died from an infected wound.

Famous Sufferers: Syphilis

Idi Amin   Charles Baudelaire   Al Capone
Christopher Columbus   Hernan Cortes   Guy de Maupassant
Isak Dinesen (Karen Blixen)   Gustave Flaubert   King Henry VIII
Abraham Lincoln   Friedrich Nietzsche   Franz Schubert
Robert Schumann   Bedrich Smetana   Bram Stoker

---

15 January: William Prout (1785-1850)
Physician and chemist; suggested hydrogen first matter (*prote hyle*)
from which all elements composed

PANACEAS

A panacea (Greek, literally a cure-all) is a substance that cures all ills. It is also known as a catholicon. Panacea was the daughter of the Greek god of Medicine Asklepios. Panaceas that have been mentioned in legend include:

Achilles' spear
Mentioned by Shakespeare in Henry VI part II: "Whose smile and frown, like to Achilles' spear, Is able with the change to kill and cure."

Aladdin's ring   Fierabras's balsam

Medea's cauldron
In which she was able to restore the dead to life and the old to youth; mentioned by William Congreve in "Love for Love": "Get thee Medea's kettle and be boiled anew."

The panthera bone
Which Reynard the Fox sent to the queen in the form of a comb, mentioned by Hendrik van Alkmaar in his legend of Reynard the Fox (Van den Vos Reynaerde, 1498): "more lustrous than the rainbow, more odoriferous than any perfume, a charm against every ill, and a universal panacea."

Prince Ahmed's apple
Mentioned in the Arabian Nights Entertainment.

The Promethean unguent
Made from a herb that had been touched by a drop of blood shed by Prometheus; Medea gave some to Jason and it made his body invulnerable to fire and the sword.

Sir Gilbert's sword
Mentioned by Thomas Malory in his History of Prince Arthur: "Sir Launcelot touched the wounds of Sir Meliot with Sir Gilbert's sword, and wiped them with the cerecloth, and anon a wholer man was he never in all his life."

"Physitions deafen our eares with the
Honorificabilitudinitatibus of their heauenly Panachea."
Nashe *Lenten Stuffe* (1599)

---

21 January: Konrad Bloch (1912-2000)
Regulation of cholesterol metabolism, Nobel prize 1964

A SMATTERING OF MEDICAL JARGON

Alopecia	baldness
Borborygmi	stomach rumblings
Carphology	plucking the bedclothes; woolgathering
Crepitations	crackles (heard in the lungs)
Dermatoglyphics	fingerprints, or more generally skin markings
Ecchymosis	bruising
Exanthem	rash
Expectoration	coughing up; loosely, spitting
Floccillation	plucking the bedclothes; woolgathering
Icterus	jaundice
Neoplasm	cancer
Nictation or nictitation	winking or blinking
Pandiculation	yawning
Proctalgia fugax	intense anal pain of unknown origin
Rhonchi	wheezes
Singultus	hiccup
Sternutation	sneezing
Strangury	painful urination
Tenesmus	painful defaecation
Urticaria	hives

LEGENDS: SIR THOMAS BROWNE

Sir Thomas Browne (1605-1682) was an English physician and author of a number of works that displayed his talents in several fields of learning, including science, religion, and the esoteric. Though he was known as Sir Thomas Browne, all his works were published under the name Thomas Brown. His book *Religio Medici* (1635) is Browne's statement of his mystical religious creed, his view as a doctor of God and the Church. In the first part he discourses on God and faith and in the second part on love of men. He has a polysyllabic Latinate style: "Acquaint thyself with the choragium of the stars". His other principal works included *Pseudodoxia Epidemica, Hydriotaphia or Urn-Burial or A Brief Discourse on the Sepulchral Urns lately found in Norfolk*, and *The Garden of Cyrus or The Quincunciall Lozenge, or Network Plantations of the Ancients, Artificially, Naturally, and Mystically Considered.*

---

27 January: John Carew Eccles (1903-1997)
Neurophysiologist, Nobel prize 1963 for elucidation of the ionic mechanisms involved in nerve conduction

MEDICAL BANDS' NAMES

Adema[1]
Anthrax
Collapsed Lung
The Cure
Doctor and the Medics
Dr Feelgood
Dr Hook
Dr Octagon
Doctor Spin
Heart
Lacrimosa
Madness
Morphine
R.E.M.[2]
St Vitus' Dance
The Strokes
Suicide Machines
Third Eye Blind[3]
X-ray Spex

[1] Adapted from edema, the American spelling of oedema
(abnormal accumulation of fluid in tissues or body cavities)
[2] From Rapid Eye Movement, the dream stage of sleep (Stage 5)
[3] The third eye is another name for the pineal gland

MEDICAL POETS

Dannie Abse
Mark Akenside
Thomas Lovell Beddoes
Sir Robert Seymour Bridges
Erasmus Darwin
Oliver Wendell Holmes
John Keats
Samuel Garth
Henry Vaughan
William Carlos Williams

28 January: Robert William Holley (1922-1993)
Structure of nucleic acids, Nobel prize 1968

DOCTORS IN OPERA

Doctor und Apotheker (1786)
Karl Ditters von Dittersdorf

Doctor Bartolo
The old doctor of Seville in Wolfgang Amadeus Mozart's *Le Nozze di Figaro*
(1786), Rossini's *Il Barbiere di Siviglia* (1816), and other operas based
on the Figaro plays by Beaumarchais.

Unnamed Doctor
Mozart's *Cosi Fan Tutte* (1790)
The maid Despina in disguise cures victims of poisons by waving a magnet
over them, claiming that she is a disciple of Dr Franz Anton Mesmer, the
founder of mesmerism.

Dr Dulcamara
Gaetano Donizetti's *L'Elisir d'Amore* (1832)
Dulcamara uses "bordo", or Bordeaux wine, effective against
everything from aches to lovesickness.
W S Gilbert, before his association with Sir Arthur Sullivan, wrote a burlesque
entitled *Dulcamara, or The Little Duck and the Great Quack* (1866).

Dr Grenvil
Giuseppe Verdi's *La Traviata* (1853)
A Parisian physician, who tries to cheer up the dying Violetta Valery,
while quietly telling her maid that she only has a few hours to live.

Dr Miracle
Georges Bizet's *Le Docteur Miracle* (1857)
Silvio, disguised as a doctor, proclaims that the only cure for a poisoned
omelette that the anti-military official has eaten is for him to marry
the official's daughter, Laurette.

Unnamed Doctor
Verdi's *La Forza del Destino* (1862)
A Spanish military surgeon, who, at the Battle of Velletri,
successfully extracts a bullet from the breast of the wounded
Alvaro, thus saving his life.

---

30 January: William Jenner (1815-98)
Invention of vaccination

DOCTORS IN OPERA (cont'd)

Dr Miracle
Jacques Offenbach's *The Tales of Hoffman* (1881)
Prescribed mysterious flagons of potions for his patient Antonia which
were to be drunk each morning.

Dr Spinellochio
Giacomo Puccini's *Gianni Schicchi* (1918)
A Florentine physician, who is deceived into thinking that he has
revived a dead corpse, when in fact it has been replaced by a live body.

LEECH'S LOGODAEDALY

Syngenesiotransplantation (25)
Transplantation of tissues between closely related people

Cystoureteropyelonephritis (26)
Inflammation of the entire urinary tract

Pneumoencephalographically (26)
Relating to an X-ray of the brain that involves injecting air into the cerebral
ventricles via the spinal cord

Encephalomyeloradiculoneuritis (30)
Inflammation of the whole of the nervous system (another term for Guillain-
Barré syndrome, famous sufferers of which have included Joseph Heller and
Tony Wedgwood-Benn)

Hepaticocholangiocholecystenterostomotically (44)
Relating to the creation of a passage from the gallbladder and hepatic duct into
the intestine

Pneumonoultramicroscopicsilicovolcanoconiosis (45)
A spurious word supposedly meaning lung damage due to inhalation of very
fine particles of silica

---

3 February: Elizabeth Blackwell (1821-1910)
The first woman in Britain to be registered as a doctor

CARRY ON FILMS

This long-running series of low-budget British comedy movies was made at Pinewood Studios in Windsor, England, and included four films set in hospitals, all directed by Gerald Thomas. The enduring character was the stern Matron, played by Hattie Jacques, who appeared in all four films.

Carry On Nurse (1959; 86 minutes, black and white). Set in Haven Hospital, where a group of men on a ward staffed by strict nurses and snobbish doctors create havoc. The film starred Hatti Jacques in her debut as Matron, with Kenneth Williams as Oliver Reckitt, the only patient willing to stand up to her. Additional characters included the bumbling Nurse Dawson (Joan Sims), Jack Bell (Leslie Phillips) who undergoes DIY bunion surgery, and a Colonel (Wilfred Hyde-White) who is a major nuisance.

Carry On Doctor (1967; 94 minutes, colour). The popular Dr Kilmore (Jim Dale) is sacked after being discovered in a compromising position on the roof of the nurses' home. The patients are determined not to lose him, and so take on the mighty team of the registrar Dr Tinkle (Kenneth Williams) and the overpowering Matron (Hatti Jacques), the film ending with their exacted revenge. A side plot has Frankie Howerd (as Francis Bigger, a famous faith healer) hurting his back and thinking he's dying.

Carry On Again Doctor (1969; 89 minutes, colour). After disgracing himself at a hospital party, Dr James Nookey (played by Jim Dale) gets conned into taking the post at a medical mission in the rain-swamped, mosquito-ridden Beatific Islands. The mission orderly, Gladstone Screwer (Sid James), has a magic potion for instant weight loss, which Dr Nookey takes back and uses to open a very successful clinic.

---

5 February: Alan Lloyd Hodgkin (1914-1998)
Neurophysiologist, Nobel prize 1963 shared with Eccles (page 17)

CARRY ON FILMS (carried on)

Carry On Matron (1972; 87 minutes, colour). A gang of thieves, including Sid Carter (played by Sid James), plan to steal a shipment of contraceptive pills from Finisham Maternity Hospital by assuming disguises and infiltrating the hospital. The doctors and nurses, including the hypochondriac consultant Sir Bernard Cutting (Kenneth Williams) and Matron (Hattie Jacques), somehow keep getting in their way.

CLASSICS: THE ANATOMY LESSON OF DR NICOLAES TULP

This is a famous painting (1632) by Rembrandt van Rijn, currently residing in the Mauritshuis, The Hague. Commissioned by the Amsterdam Company of Surgeons, the painting portrays Dr Tulp, a Dutch physician and one of the earliest forensic pathologists, pulling a tendon from the forearm of a dissected cadaver (of an executed criminal) with one hand and reproducing that motion with his other. Dr Tulp's audience is principally made up of wealthy middle-class citizens of Amsterdam, of whom only two are physicians.

Rembrandt based the painting on Thomas de Keyzer's *Anatomy Lesson of Dr Sebastian Egbertsz* (1619). However, this was not a true anatomical lesson in the 17th century sense of the term, as the most perishable parts of the body (the viscera and the contents of the chest) have not been first dissected out, only the left forearm. Dr Tulp has not been through all the stages of a teaching dissection; he merely demonstrates the superficial flexor tendons on the cadaver (erroneously arising from the extensor insertion) and the effect of his own tendons' contraction on the small joints of his own hand (the effect of Tulp's wrist being held in extension accentuating the depiction of movement in the painting). Tulp also described beri-beri and the ileocaecal valve (Tulp's valve) and wrote the first Amsterdam pharmacopoeia and *Observationes Medicae* (1641).

---

6 February: William Parry Murphy (1892-1987)
Discovery of liver therapy for pernicious anaemia, Nobel prize 1934

ETYMOLOGY: CHICKENPOX

An Arabic word, sikka[h], a coin die, was used to name the mint in Venice, the zecca, which produced the zecchino, a coin that came to be known in English as a chequeen. In *Pericles, Prince of Tyre* (4:2:28 or 16:24, depending on which edition of William Shakespeare you read) Pandar says, "three or four thousand chequeens were as pretty a proportion to live quietly, and so give over." In Shakespeare's time, a chequeen was a gold coin worth about eight old shillings (40p). Through French, the zecchino got the name sequin, which was later devalued and came to mean a cheap sparkling decoration e.g. on a dress.

But in the 15th century, the chequeen travelled to India, where it became a chicken or a chick, a coin worth about four rupees. And the earlier form of the word also survived there, as a sicca rupee, a newly minted silver coin held to be worth more than a worn one. In their Anglo-Indian dictionary of 1886, *Hobson-Jobson*, Yule and Burnell conjectured that chicken hazard, a dice game played for small stakes, "chicken stakes," came from the chequeen. So perhaps the chickenpox was merely as you might say a catchpenny, a trifling disease.

LOST WORDS

These terms are no longer in use in modern medicine:

Anasarca   Dropsy   Melancholia
Apoplexy   Exuberant   Neurasthenia*
Catarrh   Granulations   Phthisis
Cerebral softening   Grippe   Scrofula
Consumption   Laudable pus   Vapours
Lumbago

* Rarely used but still listed (code F48.0) in the 10th revision of the International Statistical Classification of Diseases and Related Health Problems (ICD-10)

WORLD WAR I AMBULANCE DRIVERS

e. e. cummings   Walt Disney   John Dos Passos
Dashiell Hammett   Ernest Hemingway   W. Somerset Maugham
Archibald MacLeish

---

7 February: Ulf Savante Von Euler (1905-1983)
Description of sympathetic neurotransmitters, Nobel prize 1970

FAMOUS SUFFERERS: GOUT

Robert Browning   Samuel Taylor Coleridge   Erasmus
Benjamin Franklin   King George IV*   Edward Gibbon
King Henry VIII   Thomas Jefferson   Samuel Johnson
Immanuel Kant   John Milton   Isaac Newton
Alfred Lord Tennyson   Leonardo da Vinci

*Percy Bysshe Shelley renamed George IV "Swellfoot the Tyrant" in his play *Oedipus Tyrannus; or, Swellfoot the Tyrant*, a satirical drama on the adultery trial of Queen Caroline.

ONDINE'S CURSE

Ondine's curse (the congenital central hypoventilation syndrome) is a disease of the respiratory centre in the brain stem, in which respiration stops when the afflicted individual goes to sleep. The condition was first described in 1962 by Severinghaus and Mitchell (*Clinical Research* 1962; 10: 122).

In Roman and other central European forms of mythology, Ondine was a water nymph who was created without a soul, but would gain one if she married a mortal man and bore his child. She fell in love with a knight called Huldbrand, married him, and bore his child. He promised that his every waking breath would be a pledge of his love, but when she found him asleep in the arms of another woman, Bertalda, Ondine cursed him that when he fell asleep he would stop breathing.

Ondine was one of Paracelsus's four elemental spirits, gnomes, sylphs, salamanders, and ondines, which represented the Hippocratic elements earth, air, fire, and water. The alternative spelling Undine, reflects its origin in the Latin word for a wave, unda.

Ondine (or Undine) was the subject of:

A novel, Undine, by Friedrich de la Motte Fouqué (1811), translated from the German by George Soane (1818) and Edmund Gosse (1896)
Operas by E T A Hoffmann (1816) and Albert Lortzing (1845)
A piano piece (part of Gaspard de la Nuit) by Maurice Ravel (1908)
A ballet by Hans Werner Henze (1958), choreographed by Frederick Ashton
A novel, Undine, by Olive Schreiner (1929)

---

9 February: François Jacob (1910-1976)
Bacterial geneticist, Nobel prize 1965 for work on the genetic control of enzyme and virus synthesis

---

IG® NOBEL PRIZES

These "alternative" annual prizes, presented at Harvard and organized by the Annals of Improbable Research (AIR), celebrate the world of weird and wonderful research, and in particular, work that is amusing, informative, and wacky. Categories are diverse, and include physics, economics, literature, and peace. Listed below are all the past winners in medicine:

1991
Alan Kligerman (USA)
Anti-gas liquids that prevent bloat, gassiness and embarrassment

1992
F. Kanda *et al.* (Japan)
Elucidation of chemical compounds responsible for foot malodour

1993
James Nolan *et al.* (USA)
Acute management of the zipper-entrapped penis

1994
Joint winners: (1) Patient X and (2) Drs Richard Dart and Richard Gustafson (USA)
(1) Rattlesnake bite victim's determination to use electroshock as therapy (via car sparkplug wires attached to his lip and engine revved to 2000 rpm for 5 minutes)
(2) For the subsequent publication "Failure of electric shock treatment for rattlesnake envenomation"

1995
Marcia Buebel *et al.* (USA)
The effects of unilateral forced nostril breathing on cognition

1996
Lead researchers and chairmen of several tobacco companies (USA)
For discovery and subsequent testimony to the US Congress that nicotine is not addictive

---

9 February: Lydia E Pinkham (1819-83)
"Lily: the Pink", who "invented medicinal compound"

IG® NOBEL PRIZES (cont'd)

1997
Carl Charnetski *et al.* (USA)
Listening to elevator Muzak stimulates immunoglobulin A (IgA) production, and thus may help prevent the common cold

1998
Patient Y and his doctors Caroline Mills *et al.* (Wales)
For the publication "A man who pricked his finger and smelled putrid for 5 years"

1999
Dr Arvid Vatle (Norway)
For carefully collecting, classifying, and contemplating which kinds of containers his patients chose when submitting urine samples

2000
Willibrord Scultz *et al.* (Netherlands)
Magnetic Resonance Imaging of male and female genitals during coitus and female sexual arousal

2001
Peter Barss (Canada)
Injuries due to falling coconuts

2002
Chris McManus (England)
Scrotal asymmetry in man and in ancient sculpture

2003
Eleanor Maguire *et al.* (England)
Brains of London taxi drivers are more highly developed than those of their fellow citizens

2004
Steven Stack and James Gundlach (USA)
The effect of country music on suicide

---

10 February: John Franklin Enders (1897-1985)
Polio virologist, Nobel prize 1954

AGATHA CHRISTIE: THALLIUM POISONING AND THE BOVINGDON BUG

The Pale Horse (1961) was one of Agatha Christie's favourite books. The title referred to the Revelation of St John the Divine (Chapter 6, verse 8): "And I looked, and behold a pale horse: and his name that sat on him was Death, and Hell followed with him..."

Thallium poisoning was the murder method of choice; the victims include Thomasina Tuckerton, who has her hair pulled out by another woman in a brawl. Baldness is one of the signs of thallium poisoning, along with a mixed motor and sensory neuropathy. Antidotes to thallium poisoning include Prussian blue and dimercaprol (British Anti-Lewisite or BAL).

Christie received a letter dated June 15, 1975 from a woman who had recognized the attempted murder of a man by his wife with thallium. She stated,

> "But of this I am quite, quite certain - had I not read *The Pale Horse* and thus learned of the effects of thallium poisoning, X would not have survived; it was only the prompt medication which saved him; and the doctors, even if he had gone to the hospital, would not have known in time what his trouble was."

In 1977 a nurse in the Hammersmith Hospital in London made the same diagnosis in a 19-month-old baby who had been flown from Qatar with a mysterious illness.

In 1971, six workers at Hadlands Equipment Works in the town of Bovingdon, Hertfordshire died of an unknown illness, symptoms of which included vomiting, weakness, paralysis, and hallucinations. The illness came to be known as the "Bovingdon Bug". Dr Hugh Johnson, a forensic specialist, who was a friend of one of the Scotland Yard detectives assigned to the case, remarked over lunch that the workers' symptoms were reminiscent of thallium overdose, which he had read about in *The Pale Horse*. One of the workers at the plant, Frederick Graham Young, seemed to have intimate knowledge of the above symptoms and the police eventually searched his flat in Hemel Hempstead and found large quantities of thallium, whereupon Young confessed to the six murders. Christie at she hoped "this felon hadn't read her book and learned from it". Fortunately for the Yard, Dr Johnson had!

---

12 February: Jan Swammerdam (1637-80)
Discovery of red blood cells

CLASSICS: THE ANATOMY OF MELANCHOLY

Robert Burton (1577-1640), who spent most of his life as a vicar at St Thomas' church in Oxford, is best remembered for his classic book *The Anatomy of Melancholy*, first published at Oxford in 1621 under the pseudonym Democritus Junior, although his real name did appear in the first edition. This is a large rambling tome of philosophical and scientific reflections about diseases of the mind and diseases in general, with discourses on the anatomy of the body and the anatomy of the soul. It has been described as one of the oddest, wittiest, and most learned books in English literature. Burton described his masterwork as "a rhapsody of rags gathered from several dunghills, excrements of authors, toys and fopperies confusedly tumbled out." The book is divided into three partitions: the first defines and describes various types of melancholy; the second advances various cures; and the third discusses love melancholy and religious melancholy. Burton concludes at the end of the book that the whole world is mad. Burton's other works included *Philosophaster* (1606), a Latin comedy about charlatanism.

HISTORICAL ALLUSIONS: SUBSTANCES

Cobalt
1683, from German kobold "goblin"; Harz Mountains silver miners' term for rock laced with arsenic and sulphur, from which the metal was extracted. Its discovery is usually credited to the Swedish chemist George Brandt (1733).

Coca-Cola
1886, invented in Atlanta, Georgia by Dr John S. Pemberton; original ingredients were derived from cocoa leaves and cola nuts. The original version contained minute amounts of cocaine until 1909.

Limey
1857; short for lime-juicer, in derisive reference to the British Navy's policy, begun in 1795, of issuing limejuice on ships to sailors in order to prevent scurvy.

---

13 February: John Hunter (1728-93)
Scottish anatomist and surgeon

AUTOPATHOGRAPHY

A biography is a book about someone's life; a pathography is a book about someone's illness; and an autopathography is a pathography written by the patient. Freud seems to have been the first to use the word pathography, and the earliest use of the word autopathography that we have found is in the title of an article by Clarence B. Farrar in *The American Journal of Insanity* in 1911 (volume 67, part 4). Some autopathographies that are worth reading (see *British Medical Journal* 2000; 321: 1599-1602) include:

- *A Bomb in the Brain* by Steve Fishman - how a severe headache led to the neurosurgeon's knife and post-surgical epilepsy; a model of scientific journalism.
- *C Because Cowards Get Cancer Too* by John Diamond - the best known of modern accounts; Diamond is amusing, unsentimental, and analytical. He is particularly good on his reasons for rejecting all forms of alternative medicine.
- *Metal Jam* and *Seized*, both by Teresa McLean - who is unusual in having written autopathographies about two distinct illnesses: diabetes and epilepsy; in both cases, some aspects of her medical care left something to be desired, but McLean, showing no hint of rancour, gives clear accounts of the diseases and how she struggled with them.
- *No Time to Die* by Liz Tilberis - ovarian cancer.
- *Man to Man. Surviving Prostate Cancer* by Michael Korda
- *A Journey Round My Skull* by Frigyes Karinthy - contains a riveting account of brain surgery under local anaesthetic.
- *Darkness Visible* by William Styron - a convincing account of what it is like to have depression.
- *The Diving-Bell and the Butterfly* by Jean-Dominique Bauby - the diary of a man almost totally paralysed by the locked-in syndrome.
- *On Blindness* by Bryan Magee and Martin Milligan - a unique exchange of letters between two philosophers about the nature of blindness.
- *Still Me* by Christopher Reeve - a dispassionate account of how the actor became paraplegic after a riding accident and how he tried to come to terms with it.

---

17 February: René Laënnec (1781-1826)
Invention of the stethoscope

NOBEL EPONYMS

Koch's postulates
Criteria to test the hypothesis that an organism has caused a disease.
Robert Koch won the Nobel prize in 1905 for "his work on tuberculosis".

Golgi bodies
Stainable bodies near the centrosome in a cell. Camillo Golgi shared the
Nobel prize in 1906 with Cajal for "work on the structure of the
nervous system".

Cajal stain
A method of staining astrocytes with a combination of gold and mercuric
chlorides. Ramón y Cajal shared the Nobel prize in 1906 with Golgi for
"work on the structure of the nervous system".

Kocher's forceps
Surgical forceps. Emil Theodor Kocher won the Nobel prize in 1909
for "his work on the physiology, pathology, and surgery of the
thyroid gland".

Carrel's mixture
A mixture of paraffin, beeswax, and castor oil for holding skin grafts
in place. Alexis Carrel won the Nobel prize in 1912 for "work on
vascular suturing and the grafting of blood vessels and organs".

Bordetella
A genus of micro-organisms. Jules Bordet won the Nobel prize in 1919
for "his discoveries in regard to immunity".

Hill plot and Hill coefficient
A method of analysing pharmacological data. A V Hill shared the Nobel
prize with Meyerhof in 1922 for "his discovery relating to the production
of heat in the muscles".

Embden-Meyerhof pathway
A set of biochemical reactions in cells. Otto Fritz Meyerhof shared the Nobel
prize with Hill in 1922 for "his discovery of the fixed relationship between
the consumption of oxygen and the metabolism of lactic acid in muscle".

---

18 February: Marshall Hall (1790-1857)
Discovery of nervous reflexes

NOBEL EPONYMS (cont'd)

Einthoven triangle
A diagrammatic representation of the potential differences that generate the electrocardiogram. Willem Einthoven won the Nobel prize in 1924 for "his discovery of the mechanism of the electrocardiogram".

Landsteiner's classification
The ABO classification of blood groups. Karl Landsteiner won the Nobel prize in 1930 for "his discovery of the human blood groups".

Whipple's disease
Intestinal lipodystrophy. George Hoyt Whipple won the Nobel prize in 1934 for "discoveries concerning liver therapy against anaemia".

Szent-Györgyi reaction
The reaction of ascorbic acid with ferrous sulphate. Albert Szent-Györgyi won the Nobel prize in 1937 for "his discoveries in connection with the biological combustion processes".

Cori cycle
The glucose-lactate cycle of reactions in muscle. Carl Ferdinand Cori and his wife Gerty won the Nobel prize in 1947 for their "discovery of the course of the catalytic conversion of glycogen".

Krebs cycle
The citric acid cycle of reactions in cells. Hans Krebs won the Nobel prize in 1953 for "his discovery of the citric acid cycle".

Hodgkin-Huxley equation
An equation describing the propagation of nerve impulses. Alan Hodgkin and Andrew Huxley won the Nobel prize in 1963 for "studies of the ionic mechanisms involved in excitation and inhibition in peripheral and central portions of the nerve cell membrane".

---

21 February: Carl Peter Henrik Dam (1895-1976)
Discovery of vitamin K, Nobel prize 1943

NOBEL EPONYMS (cont'd)

Rous sarcoma

A tumour caused by a virus. Francis Peyton Rous won the Nobel prize in 1966 for "his work on tumour-inducing viruses in chickens".

Luria-Delbruck distribution

A probability distribution relating to cell growth. Salvador Luria and Max Delbrück won the Nobel prize in 1969 for their "discoveries concerning the replication mechanism and the genetic structure of viruses".

Dulbecco's medium

A solution used in physiological experiments. Renato Dulbecco won the Nobel prize in 1975 for "discoveries concerning the interaction between tumour viruses and the genetic material of the cell".

Hounsfield number

A measure of the intensity of the signal on a CT scan. Sir Godfrey Hounsfield won the Nobel prize in 1979 for "his contributions to the development of the X-ray scanning system, computerized axial tomography".

SLANGING THE DOCTOR

"Here, said he, taking some dice out of his pockets, here are the little doctors which cure the distempers of the purse" (Tom Jones, by Henry Fielding*)*

To doctor	**Doctor Jim**
To tamper with, dope	*A soft felt hat*
Doctor Draw-fart	**Doctor Johnson**
An itinerant quack	*John Thomas*
Doctor Doddypoll	**The doctor's curse**
A fool or a doll	*Calomel*

---

22 February: Renato Dulbecco (1914-)
Interaction between tumour virus and cell genetic material,
Nobel prize 1975

KOCH'S POSTULATES

1. The micro-organism must be observed in every case of the disease.
2. The micro-organism must be isolated and grown in pure culture.
3. The pure culture must, when inoculated into a susceptible animal,
reproduce the disease.
4. The micro-organism must be observed in and recovered from the
experimentally diseased animal.

PIECES OF POETRY: ANTISEPSIS

Who dream'd that living air poison'd our SURGERY, coating
All our sheeny weapons with germs of an invisible death,
Till he saw the sterile steel work with immunity, and save
Quickly as its warring scimitars of victory had slain?
Saw what school-tradition for nature's kind method admir'd,
—In those lifedraining slow cures and bedridden agues,—
Forgotten, or condemn'd as want of care in a surgeon?

Extract from Robert Bridges,
Wintry Delights (1903)

DEATHLY BOOKS

Old Mortality by Sir Walter Scott (1816)
Death in Venice by Thomas Mann (1912)
Death Comes for the Archbishop by Willa Cather (1927)
Death of a Hero by Richard Aldington (1929)
Totentanz by Bernhard Kellerman (1948)
Death of a Salesman by Arthur Miller (1949)
The Death of William Posters by Alan Sillitoe (1965)
Death Goes Better with Coca-Cola by Dave Godfrey (1967)
Death Kit by Susan Sontag (1967)
Death of the Fox by George Garrett (1971)
Dead Babies by Martin Amis (1975)
The Dead Father by Donald Barthelme (1975)
Danse Macabre by Stephen King (1981)
A Dead Man in Deptford by Anthony Burgess (1993)

---

23 February: Allan MacLeod Cormack (1924-1998)
Development of CT scanning, Nobel prize 1979

ETYMOLOGY: MEDICAL GRAPES

In Latin, the word for a bunch of grapes was racemus. In 1822 Kestner isolated an acid from grapes, and Gay-Lussac called it racemic acid. Racemic acid was in all respects chemically identical to tartaric acid, except that it did not rotate polarized light, a phenomenon described by Jean-Baptiste Biot, who postulated molecular asymmetry. Later Louis Pasteur crystallized racemic acid and saw in his microscope that it contained two types of crystal, left-handed and right-handed; when he physically teased them apart, he found that a solution of one behaved like ordinary tartaric acid, while a solution of the other rotated light in the opposite direction. Racemic acid, being a mixture of the two, was neutral to polarized light. So the term racemate was adopted to describe a mixture of equal amounts of two stereoisomers.

Here are some medical grapes:

- Uvea and uvula are from the Latin word for a single grape, uva. The uvea was originally the choroid surface of the eye (because it looked like the skin of a grape), and later the layer of pigmented cells forming the posterior covering of the iris; now it is the iris, ciliary, and choroid taken as a unit; the uvula at the back of the palate looks like the little grape that its name implies.
- Pyruvic acid (Greek pur, fire) is formed by distillation of racemic acid, the acid obtained from grapes.
- Staphylitis, inflammation of the uvula, staphyloma, an inflammatory protrusion of the cornea or sclera, and staphylococci, which cluster in bunches like grapes, are all from the Greek word for a bunch of grapes, staphule.
- Uva and staphylos combined give us the bearberry, *Arctostaphylos uva-ursi* (Arctostaphylos = bear + grape; uva-ursi = grape + bear). Uva-ursi contains an astringent substance called arbutin and was at one time listed in the *British Pharmacopoeia* as a diuretic and urinary antiseptic.
- Ephedrine, a sympathomimetic alkaloid, gets its name from *Ephedra*, also called the sea grape, because it grows in clusters.
- Bagassosis, a lung disease, is caused by the inhalation of a dry refuse formed in sugar making, from the Spanish word bagazo, which refers to the residue of grapes left after pressing.

---

26 February: Emile Coué (1857-1926)
Pharmacist who discovered autosuggestion

AYAHUASCA

Ayahuasca is a South American psychotropic beverage prepared from mixtures of plants (e.g. *Psychotria viridis* and *Banisteriopsis caapi* vine) native to the Amazon River Basin. The mixture contains a powerful hallucinogen, dimethyltryptamine (the active ingredient in mescaline and magic mushrooms), which stimulates receptors in the brain responsible for the actions of serotonin (5-hydroxytryptamine), and a group of substances known as beta-carbolines (harmine, harmaline, and tetrahydroharmine), which inhibit the breakdown of serotonin, thus enhancing its actions further. The name ayahuasca is used in Bolivia, Ecuador, and Peru, while in Brazil and Colombia it is known as *caapi* and in Colombia also as *yagé*. It is used by shamans and in religious ceremonies.

LEGENDS: AARON OF ALEXANDRIA

A Greek physician (fl. between 610 and 641 AD), who wrote in Syriac. Most of his writings have been lost. His *Pandect*, a Greek medical encyclopaedia in 30 sections, was the first book translated from Syriac into Arabic by Masarjawaih of Basra in 683 under the title *Qarabahin*.

ANCIENT CURES: EPILEPSY

Arsenic
Bolus of human mummy
Borax
Boy's urine
Cod liver oil
Distilled human skull
Dried human heart
Gladiator blood (warm)
Horse excrement
Goose excrement
Mouse excrement
Strychnine

27 February: Charles Herbert Best (1899-1978)
Discovery of insulin

JOINING THE DOTS

DoTS stands for **D**ose, **T**ime, and **S**usceptibility (*BMJ* 2003; 327: 1222-5). The DoTS system has been used to classify adverse drug reactions.

There are three types of **dose-related** adverse reactions:

1. *Toxic reactions* occur at supratherapeutic concentrations of the drug.
2. *Collateral reactions* occur at therapeutic concentrations of the drug.
3. *Hypersusceptibility reactions* occur at subtherapeutic concentrations of the drug.

There are two types of **time-related** adverse effects -
time-dependent and *time-independent*.

Time-independent reactions can occur at any time during treatment.

There are six types of *time-dependent* effects:

1. *Rapid reactions* occur only when a drug is administered too rapidly.
2. *First dose reactions* occur after the first dose of a course of treatment and not necessarily thereafter.
3. *Early reactions* occur early in treatment then abate with continuing treatment.
4. *Intermediate reactions* occur after some delay; however, if a reaction has not occurred after a certain time, there is little or no risk that it will occur later.
5. *Late reactions* occur rarely or not at all at the beginning of treatment, but the risk increases with continued or repeated exposure.
6. *Delayed reactions* are observed some time after exposure, even if the drug is withdrawn before the reaction appears.

There are numerous **susceptibility factors**. The important groups can be remembered using the mnemonic **GASPED**:
Genetic   **A**ge-related   **S**ex-related   **P**hysiological factors
Exogenous factors (e.g. drugs)   **D**iseases (e.g. renal, hepatic)

28 February: Peter Brian Medawar (1915-1987)
Discovery of acquired immunological tolerance, Nobel prize 1960

AYURVEDIC MEDICINE

The Ayurvedic system (*Ayus* = longevity and *Veda* = knowledge in Sanskrit) is a holistic medicinal philosophy originating among the Brahmin sages of ancient India around 3000-5000 years ago. For every disease there is a wealth of information available, including aetiology, definition, etymology, symptoms, pathophysiology, medications, surgery, and lifestyle recommendations, in a similar vein to modern Western medicine. Indeed, Patna in India is credited as probably the world's first organized hospital-based health care system. Still practised today, the eight major disciplines are as follows:

1. Kayachikitsa (internal medicine)
2. Salya tantra (surgery)
3. Salakya tantra (treatment of the ears, nose, throat, eyes, jaws, & teeth)
4. Agada tantra (toxicology)
5. Bhuta vidya (psychiatry)
6. Bala tantra (gynaecology and paediatrics)
7. Rasayana tantra (geriatrics)
8. Vajikarana tantra (sexology)

Here are some Ayurvedic remedies for:

Alcoholism	*Tamarind juice (Amlika)*
Bowel cramps	*Wheat gruel*
Carditis (rheumatic)	*Dried ginger*
Dysentery	*Dried amalaki fruit*
Epilepsy	*Brahmi of Bengal herb*
Fractured bones	*Honey (Madhu)*
Gallstone colic	*Coral tree bark (Paribhadraka)*
Headaches	*Marjoram tea*
Influenza	*Sea buckthorn fruit juice*
Jaundice	*Kutaki herb rhizome*
Kidney disorders	*Couch grass (Agropyron repens)*
Leprosy	*Tuvuraka herb seed oil*
Malaria	*Saptaparna tree bark*
Nausea	*Lime (Citrus aurantifolia)*
Ophthalmia	*Bibhitaki fruit*
Period pains	*Sweet flag rhizome*

---

28 February: Philip Showalter Hench (1896-1965)
Discovery of cortisone, Nobel prize 1950

AYURVEDIC MEDICINE (cont'd)

Quartan fever	*Powdered fruit of long pepper*
Rheumatism	*Incense tree Sallaki*
Stings	*Rauwolfia root*
Trembling	*Ghee from sheep's milk*
Ulcers	*Old ghee*
Vertigo	*Cow's milk*
Wounds	*Oil of St John's wort (Hypericum perforatum)*

SONG TITLES CONTAINING "DOCTOR"

The Doctor	Doobie Brothers
Dr Beat	Miami Sound Machine
Doctor Doctor	UFO/Thompson Twins
Dr Feelgood	Motley Crue
Dr Finlay	Andy Stewart
Dr Greenthumb	Cypress Hill
Dr Heckyll and Mr Jive	Men at Work
Doctor Jackyll & Mister Funk	Jackie Mclean
Doctor Jeep	Sisters of Mercy
Doctor Jones	Aqua
Doctor Kiss Kiss	5000 Volts
Dr Love	Tina Charles
Dr Mabuse	Propaganda
Doctor My Eyes	Jacksons
Dr Robert	The Beatles
Dr Stein	Halloween
Dr Who	Mankind
Doctorin' The House	Coldcut (Yazz & the Plastic Population)
Doctor'n' The Tardis	Timelords
Doctor's Orders	Sunny

UNSCIENTIFIC NAMES: LEPTIN

Leptin, a hormone that may be involved in obesity, has been nicknamed "The Fat Controller".

---

3 March: Arthur Kornberg (1918-)
Synthesis of RNA and DNA, Nobel prize 1959

MATCHING NAMES AND TITLES

Waters TH.
Report on the sanitary condition of certain parts of Manchester, 1853.

Diseases of the Nervous System by Russell Brain (1st edition, 1933)

Alpher RA, Bethe H, and Gamow G.
The origin of chemical elements. *The Physical Review* 1948; 73: 803-4.

Cathcart RT, Blood DW.
Effect of digitalis on the clotting of the blood in normal subjects and in patients with congestive heart failure. *Circulation* 1950; 1: 1176-81.

J Thomas, C Small.
Carcinoma of the penis in Southern India. *J Urol* 1968; 100: 520-6.

Hand CR, McFarland GB Jr.
Synovial sarcoma of the hand. *J La State Med Soc* 1970; 122: 1-5.

Waters N, Gaha TJ, Reynolds I.
Random urine analyses from drug addicts in a methadone treatment programme. *Med J Aust* 1975; 2: 170-2.

Wright PA.
The right to parenthood. *Family Law Review* 1979; 2: 173-85.

Nutt DJ, Cowen PJ, Batts CC, et al.
Repeated doses of subconvulsant doses of GABA antagonist drugs. *Psychopharmacology* 1982; 76: 84-7

Wright CV, Halpern ME.
Specification of left-right asymmetry. *Results Probl Cell Differ.* 2002; 40: 96-116.

Smith G.
Horseshoe pitchers' hot hands. *Psychon Bull Rev* 2003; 10: 753-8.

---

5 March: William Henry Beveridge (1879-1963)
Architect of the welfare state

MEDICAL GEOMETRY: SPIRALS

DNA: the double helix
The cochlea of the inner ear (Latin cochlea = a screw)
Curschmann spirals (spiral-shaped sputum in patients with bronchial asthma)
Corkscrew hairs in scurvy
Corkscrew spasm of the oesophagus
Spiral fractures of long bones
Spiral CT: a three-dimensional method of computerized tomography
Spiral arteries: spiral-shaped arteries in the placenta
Spiral ganglion: a ganglion of the eighth cranial nerve, the vestibulocochlear
The medical snake

OSLERIAN EPONYMS

William Osler (1849-1919), the Father of Modern Medicine, was born in
Ontario, Canada, and became Professor of Medicine successively at McGill
University, Montreal, the University of Pennsylvania, and Johns Hopkins
Hospital, Maryland. In 1905, he came to Oxford as the Regius Professor of
Medicine.

Osler-Rendu-Weber syndrome	Hereditary haemorrhagic telangiectasia
Osler's sign	Artificially high blood pressure reading in atherosclerosis
Osler's nodes	Painful nodules in the finger pulp in infective endocarditis
Sphryanuria Osleri	Trematode worm discovered by Osler in the gills of a newt
Filaria Osleri	Parasitic nematode worm which causes bronchopneumonia in dogs
Osler-Libman-Sacks disease	Alternative name for infective endocarditis
Osler-Vaquez disease	Polycythaemia rubra vera
Osler's phenomenon	Platelet aggregation as blood is withdrawn from the body
Osler pavilion	Tuberculosis hospital behind which Osler road ran; now the site of the John Radcliffe Hospital in Oxford

---

7 March: David Baltimore (1938-1983)
Discovery of viral reverse transcriptase, Nobel prize 1975

Proprietary formulations containing aspirin

When doctors prescribe a drug by its brand name, they can confidently expect the pharmacist to give the patient a particular compound. For example, if they prescribe Brufen the pharmacist will dispense a formulation that contains ibuprofen.

But buying drugs over the counter can be more complicated. For example, tablets with the name Anadin on the box may contain aspirin and caffeine; or aspirin, caffeine, and quinine; or aspirin, caffeine, and paracetamol; or paracetamol alone; or even ibuprofen alone. Of course, these different formulations have slightly different names, such as Anadin Extra for aspirin plus caffeine plus paracetamol, and Anadin Paracetamol for paracetamol alone, so you should be able to tell the difference.

Other common formulations that contain aspirin include:

Alka-Seltzer[1]
Askit[2]
Beecham's powders
Disprin
Lemsip
Mrs Cullen's
Nurse Sykes' powders
Phensic[3]
Veganin

[1] The formulation is an alkaline one, and in solution it effervesces like water from Nieder-Selters in Germany
[2] Sold originally without a name in Laidlaw's pharmacy in Glasgow. Mr and Mrs Laidlaw allegedly overheard two girls whispering in their shop. "You ask it," said one; "You ask it." said the other!
[3] Based on the ingredient phenacetin

Medical seeds and vegetables

Cauliflower ears	*Deformed swollen ear secondary to repetitive trauma*
Glans penis	*Terminal portion of penis (glans = acorn)*
Onion skinning	*Laminated periosteal reaction seen in Ewing's sarcoma of bone*
Potato tumour	*Carotid body neoplasm (chemodectoma)*

7 March: Julius Wagner von Jauregg (1857-1940)
Malaria treatment of syphilitic dementia, Nobel prize 1927

LEGENDS: AVICENNA

Avicenna was the Western name for Abu 'Ali al-Husayn ibn 'Abd Allah ibn Sibna (AD 980-1037), a Persian physician and philosopher whose *Canon of Medicine (al-Qanan fi at-tibb)* (1010) influenced medical practice through the Middle Ages, both in the West and in the Islamic world. He was court physician to Prince Shams ad-Dawlah in Hamdan, west central Persia and later to Ala ad-Dawlah in Isfahan, south of Tehran. The canon consisted of five books dealing with the aetiologies and treatments of a wide variety of diseases. His work, an elaboration on Galen's medical teachings, was even mentioned in the Prologue to Geoffrey Chaucer's *The Canterbury Tales*. His other famous book was *Kitab ash-shifa*, a treatise on logic and natural sciences.

NOBEL PRIZE WINNERS WHO WORKED FOR PHARMACEUTICAL COMPANIES

Gerhardt Domagk (1938)
Discovered sulphonamides while working for IG Farber Industrie in Elberfeld, Germany, as director of research

Paul Muller (1948)
Discovered DDT (dichlorodiphenyltrichloroethane), working for J. R. Geigy in Basel

John Vane (1982)
Worked on prostaglandins at the Wellcome Laboratories in Beckenham, England

James Black (1988)
Invented beta-blockers whilst working for Imperial Chemical Industries in Macclesfield, England; he later invented histamine blockers while working for Smith Kline & French

Gertrude Elion and George Hitchings (1988)
Discovered important principles for drug treatment, creating a rational method for discovering new compounds, including mercaptopurine, trimethoprim, and allopurinol, whilst working for the Wellcome Company in North Carolina, USA

---

8 March: Edward Calvin Kendall (1886-1972)
Discovery of hormones of the adrenal cortex, Nobel prize 1950

DEVICES AND THEIR INVENTORS

Computerized Axial Tomography (CT)	Sir Godfrey Hounsfield	1971
Electrical hearing aid	Miller Hutchinson	1901
Electrocardiogram (ECG)	Willem Einthoven	1903
Electroencephalogram (EEG)	Hans Berger	1924
Heart-lung machine	John Gibbon	1953
Heart valve replacement	Dwight Harken	1961
Modern hip replacement	John Charnley	1962
Hypodermic syringe	Francis Rynd	1845
Iron lung	Philip J Drinker	1929
Kidney dialysis machine	Willem J Kolff	1943
Laryngoscope	Manuel Garcia	1854
Magnetic Resonance Imaging (MRI)	Paul C Lauterbur &	
	Sir Peter Mansfield	1977
Ophthalmoscope	Charles Babbage	1847
Pacemaker	Earl Bakken	1952
Sphygmomanometer	Scipione Riva-Rocci	1896
Stethoscope	René Laënnec	1815
Ultrasound	Ian Donald	1957
X-radiography	Wilhelm Roentgen	1895

ANATOMICALLY ENTITLED: LEGS

Bury My Heart at Wounded Knee
History of the subjugation of the American Indians after the end of the Civil War by Dee Alexander Brown (1970); the title is from a poem called American Names by Stephen Vincent Benét (1931). Wounded Knee was the name of the place in South Dakota where the Teton-Sioux Indians were massacred by US troops on 29 December 1890. Brian Aldiss entitled a volume of memoirs "Bury My Heart at W. H. Smith's" (1990).

Le Genu de Claire
Film by Eric Rohmer (1970), one of his "contes moraux".

Ankle Deep
Novel by Angela Thirkell (1933). The story of a weekend of unhappy relationships.

My Left Foot
Autobiography by the Irish painter Christy Brown, so disabled that he could only write with his left foot; it was made into a film by Jim Sheridan, starring Daniel Day-Lewis, in 1989.

---

10 March: Marcello Malpighi (1628-94)
Italian anatomist

Physician's proverbs

If the doctor cures, the sun sees it;
but if he kills, the Earth hides it

The doctor is often more to be feared than the disease

One doctor makes work for another

After death, the doctor

A broken apothecary,
a new doctor

An apple a day keeps the doctor away

Death defies the doctor

Where the sun enters,
the doctor does not

There is no physician like a true friend

A physician is an angel when employed,
but a devil when one must pay him

Every man is a physician,
save him that is sick

The physician owes all to the patient,
but the patient owes nothing to him but a little money

The best physicians are
Doctor Diet,
Doctor Quiet,
and Doctor Merryman

Physicians kill more than they cure

Where there are three physicians,
there are two atheists

14 March: Paul Ehrlich (1854-1915)
Nobel prize for side-chain theory of antibody production 1908

PHYSICIAN'S PROVERBS (cont'd)

That city is in a bad case whose physician has the gout

Feed by measure and defy the physician

Few lawyers die well,
few physicians live well

Every man is a fool or a physician

He is a fool who makes his physician his executor

Go not for every grief to the physician,
nor for every quarrel to the liar,
nor for every thirst to the pot

God heals,
and the physician has the thanks

To the gout all physicians are blind

Hide nothing from thy minister, physician and lawyer

Honour a physician before thou hast need of him

Nature, time and patience are the three great physicians

Who pays the physician does the cure

Piss clear and defy the physician

A pitiful physician spoils a sore

St Luke was a saint and a physician,
and yet he died

Words ending in -ic do mock the physician;
as hectic, paralytic, apoplectic, lethargic

---

15 March: John Snow (1813-58)
Discovery of the mode of transmission of cholera
and invention of ether anaesthesia

PHYSICIAN'S PROVERBS (cont'd)

A young physician fattens the churchyard

A good surgeon should have three diverse properties in his person:
a heart as the heart of a lion,
his eyes like the eyes of a hawk,
and his hands the hands of a woman
John Halle, surgeon (1529-68)
[To which Grimsdyke in Doctor in the House added "and the commercial
morals of a Levantine usurer"]

There is no medicine for fear but cut off the head

Medicines are not meat to live by

PAINTINGS WITH MEDICAL THEMES

An Advanced Dressing Station in France, 1918 (1918)	Henry Tonks
The Anatomy Lesson of Dr Nicolaes Tulp (1632)	Rembrandt van Rijn
Ancoats Hospital Outpatients' Hall (1952)	L. S. Lowry
Death in the Sick Room (1893)	Edvard Munch
The Doctor (c 1891)	Sir Luke Fildes
The Doctor's Visit (c 1663)	Jan Steen
Drug Store (1927)	Edward Hopper
The First Wounded, London Hospital 1914 (1915)	John Lavery
The Hospital at Arles (1889)	Vincent Van Gogh
The Illness of Pierrot (1859-60)	Thomas Couture
The Mission of Mercy: Florence Nightingale Receiving the Wounded at Scutari (1857)	Jerry Barrett
The Physician (1653)	Gerrit Dou
Portrait of Doctor Gachet (1890)	Vincent Van Gogh
Science and Charity (1897)	Pablo Picasso
Self-portrait with Dr Arrieta	Francisco de Goya
Vaccination (1807)	Louis-Leopold Boilly
The Village Doctor (c 1650)	David Teniers the Younger
A Visit to Aesculapius (1880)	Sir Edward Poynter

17 March: William Withering (1741-1799)
Discovery of the medical uses of the foxglove;
first botany written in English

DRUG BRAND NAMES

Alka-Seltzer - see Proprietary Formulations Containing Aspirin

Aspirin - branded by Bayer Pharmaceuticals; *a* from acetylsalicylic acid, and *spir* from the *Spiraea ulmeria* plant (meadow-sweet of the rose family). Kurt Witthauer derived the word in 1899.

BiSoDol (antacid) - from *bi*carbonate of *so*da, plus *dol* from *dolor* (pain).

Bongela - "good gel".

Cordilox (verapamil) - derived from *cor* (Latin, heart).

Dolobid (diflunisal) - a salicylate used to treat pain (*dolor*) and given twice a day (*bid*).

Dramamine - from Diphenhy*dramine* with duplication in the middle.

Ex-Lax - excellent or *ex* (Latin, out) and *lax*ative.

Largactil (chlorpromazine) - *large activité* (from French) for extensive action.

Novocain (procaine)- from Latin *novo* (new) and *cocaine*; most local anaesthetics have names ending in -caine

Paludrine (proguanil for malaria) - from Latin *palus* for marsh.

Rennies - invented by a Yorkshireman called John *Rennie*. Originally marketed in France as "Digestif Rennies".

Viagra (sildenafil citrate) - combination of the words "*vig*orous" and "Ni*agra*" Falls.

Vick - named after Dr Joshua *Vick* in whose drugstore the inventor originally worked. Invented by Dr Vick's brother-in-law Lunsford Richardson, US druggist in Selma, North Carolina, USA. Its ingredients include menthol.

---

23 March: Daniel Bovet (1907-1992)
Pharmacologist, Nobel prize for work on several synthetic compounds including curare 1957

JOSEPH MERRICK
(THE ELEPHANT MAN)

Joseph Merrick, the famous Victorian "Elephant Man" described by Frederick Treves, has generally been supposed to have suffered from neurofibromatosis. However, it has been suggested that he had instead a rare condition known as Proteus syndrome (*BMJ* 1986;293:683-5). This diagnosis is supported by evidence from X-rays and CT scans of Merrick's remains. Both conditions are hamartoses, but while neurofibromatosis consists of multiple tumours of nerve cells, Proteus syndrome, a somatic mosaicism, involves abnormal growth of bone and soft tissues.

John Hurt's portrayal of Merrick in David Lynch's 1980 film *The Elephant Man* was reminiscent of cinematic portrayals of Quasimodo, by Lon Chaney in 1923, Anthony Quinn in 1957, and most memorably Charles Laughton in 1939. In *Notre Dame de Paris*, Hugo wrote that Quasimodo looked like a giant broken and badly repaired, with a warty brow, a tetrahedral nose and a horseshoe mouth, misshapen legs of unequal length that looked like two sickles joined at the handles, and a hump between the shoulders balanced by one in front. Perhaps he had the Proteus syndrome?

LEGENDS: PARACELSUS

The pseudonym adopted by the Swiss physician and alchemist Theophrastus Bombastus von Hohenheim (1493-1541), because he considered himself to be superior to (Greek *para*, beyond) the 1st century physician Celsus. He learned about the properties of metals and their ores from working in Tyrolean mines and then became a physician. He believed that knowledge of alchemy and the physical sciences was essential for the practice of medicine.

FAMOUS SUFFERERS:
RHEUMATOID ARTHRITIS

Constantine	*Raoul Dufy*
Mary Queen of Scots	*Pierre-Auguste Renoir*
Peter Paul Rubens	*Rosemary Sutcliff*
Paul Verlaine	*James Madison*

---

26 March: Bernard Katz (1911-2003)
Work on neurotransmitters, Nobel prize 1970

DRUGS FROM PLANTS

Aconite	Blue-flowered monkswood (*Aconitum napellus*)
Artemether	Qinghao (*Artemisia annua*)
Atropine	Deadly nightshade (*Atropa belladonna*)
Cardiac glycosides	Foxglove (*Digitalis lanata*)
Cocaine	Coca (*Erythroxylon coca*)
Colchicine	Autumn crocus (*Colchicum autumnale*)
Curare	Pareira (*Chondrodendron tomentosum*)
Hyoscine	Thorn apple (*Datura stramonium*)
Opiates	Opium poppy (*Papaver somniferum*)
Physostigmine	Calabar bean (*Physostigma venenosum*)
Reserpine	Indian snake-bite root rauwolfia (*Rauwolfia serpentina*)
Strychnine	Nux vomica (*Strychnos nux vomica*)
Paclitaxel	Pacific yew tree (*Taxus brevifolia*)
Theophylline	Tea plant (*Camellia sinensis*)
Vincristine, vinblastine	Madagascar periwinkle (*Vinca rosea*)

EUPHEMISMS: ABORTION

Birth quota
Bring off
Criminal operation
D and C
Drop a bundle
Female pills
French renovating pills
Hoovering
Illegal operation
Misgo
Mishap
Part with child
Pick
Pregnancy interruption
Pro-choice
Procedure
Reproductive freedom
Slip
Slip a filly

---

27 March: Wilhelm Konrad von Roentgen (1845-1923)
Discovery of X-rays

ALGEBRAIC BONESETTERS

From the Arabic *al-jebr*, the term algebra was originally used to describe the reunion of broken parts, specifically the surgical treatment of fractures or bone setting. It was later extended to the mathematical science of reunion that we now call algebra, from its use in the phrase ilm al-jebr wa'l-muqabalah ("the science of reunion and equation"). In Spanish, *algebrista* means both an algebraist and a bonesetter.

The word "set" has the longest entry in many dictionaries. For example, in *The Chambers Dictionary* (1993) it occupies two and a quarter columns of text, compared with the average entry, which occupies about one-fifteenth of a column. In the *Oxford English Dictionary* (2nd edition) it is allocated two substantive meanings, two verbal meanings, and an adjectival meaning, running to 25 pages, under 213 numbered headings, with many subheadings. However, only one of its meanings is medical – to set a bone.

The Bonesetter's Daughter, a book by Amy Tan (2001), revolves around the life of a young girl, LuLing, the granddaughter of the Famous Bonesetter from the village of Xian Xin (Immortal Heart) near the Mouth of the Mountain. LuLing's family, a clan of ink makers, believes itself cursed by its connection to a local doctor, who brews his potions and remedies from human bones.

HISTORICAL ALLUSIONS: DEATH

Bite the bullet
1700s, military slang, from old medical custom of patients biting bullets during operations to divert attention away from the pain

Hara-kiri
1856, Japanese, the colloquial word for what is formally called seppuku "cut open the stomach"; from hara "belly" + kiri "to cut"

Kamikaze
1945, Japanese, from kami "divine" and kaze "wind"; in folklore the name given to a typhoon which saved Japan from Mongol invasion by destroying Kublai Khan's fleet (August 1281)

---

28 March: Corneille Heymans (1892-1968)
Discovery of respiratory mechanisms, Nobel prize 1938

Diseases & Drugs named after Patients

Bacitracin	*Drug isolated from Bacillus subtilis; named after Margaret Tracy from whose skin it was isolated*
Barbiturates	*Named after a waitress called Barbara in a Munich cafe*
Cowden disease	*Multiple benign skin tumours named after Rachel Cowden*
Christmas disease (haemophilia B)	*Named after Stephen Christmas, a patient in whom the disease was studied in detail*
Duncan disease	*X-linked recessive immunodeficiency syndrome following Epstein-Barr virus (EBV) infection*
Dusard syndrome	*Named after family with congenital dysfibrinogenaemia*
Hartnup disease	*Aminoaciduria; named after original family*
HeLa cell	*Cells seen in cervical cancer; named after Henrietta Lax*
Machado-Joseph disease	*Spinocerebellar ataxia type 3; named after*
Passovoy defect	*Inherited defect leading to increased risk of haemorrhage; named after the investigated sufferer*

Eponymous Blood Groups

Diego antigen	*Common in Chinese, Japanese, and South Americans, but not in Europe; named after Venezuelan patient called Diego*
Fletcher factor	*Original name for prekallikrein; named after a patient in whom a defect was first discovered*
Gonzales blood group	*Only found in people of African descent*
Kell blood group	*Mrs Kell, the patient in whom this antigen was identified*
Kidd blood group	*Named after family in which it was first identified*
Lewis blood group	*Named after Mrs Lewis*

---

1 April: William Harvey (1578-1657)
Discovery of the circulation of the blood

ALCOHOL FACTS

Alcohol is the common name for ethanol (C_2H_5OH) or ethyl alcohol. It is present in a wide range of drinks in a wide range of concentrations:

Low-alcohol beer 0.5%   Beer 2.5-11%   Cider 3.5-5%
Table wine 9.5-15.5%   Fortified wine 16-23%
Spirits 35-55%   Absinthe 68%

Alcohol content is normally expressed as percentage by volume or weight. 100% proof is about 52% of alcohol by volume. The term proof is derived from the fact that the testing of alcohol was by the same proof houses that tested the safety of firearms. 100% proof is defined as that mixture of alcohol that can just ignite gunpowder.

In addition to alcohol, alcoholic drinks can contain other constituents called congeners, of which the commonest is fusel oil. Congeners may be present in quantities up to 0.3% of the volume of alcohol, and they contribute to the taste of the drink.

Alcohol depresses the brain, producing the well-known features of intoxication. At plasma concentrations of around 40 mg/dL (8.7 mmol/L) learned skills, including self-restraint, are impaired. Other early effects include loss of attentiveness, loss of concentration, and impaired memory; lethargy can occur. At progressively higher concentrations there are further changes in mood, behaviour, and a variety of sensory and motor functions. Alcohol causes acute drowsiness and deep sleep, and in high concentrations coma and respiratory depression. In older people sleep is later impaired. On waking there is the characteristic "hangover", with irritability, headache, belly cramps, bowel disturbance, and thirst. The cause is not known and there is no effective treatment. "Cures" include:

A large drink of water before bed; some recommend adding jalapeno peppers
Lots of sugar (e.g. a sugary drink, fruit)
Lots of salt (e.g. salty crisps)
A prairie oyster – a raw unbeaten egg in vinegar or Worcestershire sauce plus salt and pepper, swallowed rapidly
A hair of the dog e.g. 50/50 tequila and tabasco sauce
A sauna
Strong antiemetic drugs (e.g. granisetron) - not available for general use

---

3 April: James Dewey Watson (1928-)
Discovery of the structure of DNA, Nobel prize 1962

FAMOUS SUFFERERS: CONSTIPATION

Napoleon Bonaparte   Mohandas "Mahatma" K Gandhi
George Gershwin   William Henry Harrison   Howard Hughes
Henry James   Thomas Jefferson   Maximilien Robespierre

PHYSICIANS' FRUITS

Adam's apple
Laryngeal prominence in the neck

Apple core deformity
Annular constricting radiological lesion of large bowel,
often secondary to carcinoma

Apple jelly nodule
Tuberculosis of skin
Press on it with a glass and it looks like apple jelly

Berry aneurysm
Cerebral artery aneurysm

Blueberry muffin baby
Congenital toxoplasmosis

Cherry angiomas
Also known as Campbell de Morgan's spots

Grapes
(see page 34)

Lemon-on-stick appearance
Typical physical appearance of patient with Cushing's syndrome

Melon seed bodies
Seen in bursitis

Peau d'orange
Characteristic puckering of the skin overlying
breast carcinoma ("orange skin")

---

5 April: Joseph Lister (1827-1912)
Scottish surgeon, first to use antisepsis to prevent wound infection

---

PHYSICIANS' FRUITS (cont'd)

Piriform fossa
Anatomical space at the upper end of the femur in the shape of a pear

Prune belly syndrome
Congenital defect of the abdominal musculature

Redcurrant jelly
Typical stools of intussusception

Strawberry tongue
Dark red papillary projections on the tongue

Strawberry naevus
Cavernous cutaneous haemangioma

DRINKING DOCTORS (PUB NAMES)

Doctor Fosters (Chorlton-on-Medlock, near Manchester)
The Good Doctor (Sheffield)   The Doctor WG Grace (London SE20)
Dr Samuel Johnson (Langley Green)
Dr Johnson (Lichfield)   Doctor Syntax (Preston)

FAMOUS SUFFERERS: DIABETES

*Arthur Ashe   Jack Benny   James Cagney   Johnny Cash
Miles Davis   Colin Dexter   Thomas Edison
Jackie Gleason   Elvis Presley
Ernest Hemingway   Teresa McLean
Mario Puzo   Giacomo Puccini   Steve Redgrave
Sugar Ray Robinson   Spencer Tracy
Luther Vandross   Sir Andrew Lloyd Webber   HG Wells*

6 April: Feodor Felix Konrad Lynen (1911-1979)
Regulation of cholesterol metabolism, Nobel prize 1964

Maximum Speeds of Animals
(Kilometres per Hour)

Man - sports record 1500 metres	*25.8*
Man - sports record 100 metres	*36.7*
Man - Masai warrior, carrying a spear and shield,	
chased by an African rhinoceros	*40*
African rhinoceros	*48*
Greyhound	*64*
Racehorse	*64*
Cheetah	*70*
Dragonfly	*100*
Mallard duck	*100*
Hummingbird	*100*
Homing pigeon (level flight, no wind)	*150*

Syndromes from the Nursery

Cheshire Cat syndrome
Failure to make a diagnosis because not all the signs and symptoms are present

Cinderella complex
Unconscious desire to be taken care of by others

Humpty Dumpty syndrome
Fragmentation of general surgery into several subspecialties

Mother Goose syndrome
The need to provide a wide and varied nursery education

Sleeping Beauty syndrome
A child who remains unconscious after head injury

Snow White syndrome
Loving your father and having a wicked mother

---

10 April: Bernardo Alberto Houssay (1887-1971)
Discovery of action of ACTH (adrenocorticotrophic hormone)
Nobel prize 1947

DANGEROUS FOODS

Artificial food colourings (e.g. tartrazine)
Can cause asthma

Aspartame
Worsens phenylketonuria

Betel nuts
Contain arecoline, which can exacerbate asthma

Broad beans
Cause haemolysis in people with glucose-6-phosphate dehydrogenase deficiency

Chocolate
Can trigger migraine; worsens hyperoxaluria

Grapefruit juice
Inhibits the metabolism of some drugs, making them more dangerous

Nuts, shellfish, molluscs
Can cause allergic reactions in susceptible individuals

Rhubarb
Worsens hyperoxaluria

PIECES OF POETRY: AGEING

What is it to grow old?
Is it to lose the glory of the form,
The lustre of the eye?
Is it for beauty to forego her wreath?
Yes, but not for this alone.

Is it to feel our strength -
Not our bloom only, but our strength - decay?
Is it to feel each limb
Grow stiffer, every function less exact,
Each nerve more weakly strung?

Extract from Matthew Arnold,
Growing Old (1867)

12 April: Otto Fritz Meyerhof (1884-1951) Biochemist, Nobel
prize for discovery relating to production of heat in muscle 1922

GESTATION PERIODS OF MAMMALS (IN DAYS)

Horse (*Equus caballus*)	336
Cattle (*Bos taurus*)	281
Man (*Homo sapiens sapiens*)	267
Chimpanzee (*Pan troglodytes*)	227
Rhesus monkey (*Macaca rhesus*)	160
Sheep (*Ovis aries*)	151
Goat (*Capra hircus*)	148
Guinea pig (*Cavia porcellus*)	68
Cat (*Felis catus*)	63
Dog (*Canis familiaris*)	63
Rabbit (*Oryctolagus cuniculus*)	31
Rat (*Rattus rattus*)	22
Mouse (*Mus musculus*)	19
Opossum (*Didelphys virginiana*)	12.5

MEN WHO PLAYED DOC HOLLIDAY IN THE MOVIES

Harvey Clark	*Law for Tombstone* (1937)
Cesar Romero	*Frontier Marshal* (1939)
Kent Taylor	*Tombstone, the Town Too Tough to Die* (1942)
Walter Huston	*The Outlaw* (1943)
Victor Mature	*My Darling Clementine* (1946)
James Griffith	*Masterson of Kansas* (1954)
Kirk Douglas	*Gunfight at the OK Corral* (1957)
Arthur Kennedy	*Cheyenne Autumn* (1964)
Jason Robards	*Hour of the Gun* (1967)
Duke Moberdy	*My Third Wife George* (1968)
Stacy Keach	*Doc* (1971)
Dennis Hopper	*Wild Times* (1980)
Jeffrey de Munn	*I Married Wyatt Earp* (1983)
Willie Nelson	*Stagecoach* (1986)
Dewey Martin	*Doc Holliday* (1988)
Val Kilmer	*Tombstone* (1993)
Dennis Quaid	*Wyatt Earp* (1994)
Mick Ford	*Strike Free* (1995)

15 April: Nicholas Tinbergen (1907-1988)
Ethologist, Nobel prize for discoveries concerning
individual and social behaviour patterns 1973

ANATOMY

Anatomy is from the Greek *ana*, up, and *temno*, I cut. In the 16th century, the word "atomy" was falsely coined from "anatomy" through aphaeresis (the removal of the supposed indefinite article an). John Gay used it in *The Beggar's Opera* (1728). When Matt of the Mint is asked what has happened to his brother, Tom, he says that he had an accident – in other words, was hanged – and having fallen into the hands of the dissectors "is among the otamies [sic] at Surgeon's Hall"(2, i).

Atomy also came to mean someone very thin, for example, in Shakespeare's *Henry IV Part 2* (1598): ". . . you starved bloodhound . . . Thou atomy, thou!" (*5, iv, 29*). Charles Dickens used the word figuratively in *Dombey and Son* (1848) (Chapter IX): "Withered atomies of teaspoons".

The word anatomy itself has featured in many titles of books, poems, songs and pieces of music, and works of art, including:

- *The Anatomy Lesson of Dr Tulp*, painting by Rembrandt (1632)
- *The Anatomy of Melancholy*, by Robert Burton (1621)
- *The Anatomist*, play by James Bridie (1930)
- *Anatomy of a Murder*, film starring James Stewart and Lee Remick, directed by Otto Preminger (1959).
- *The Anatomy Lesson*, novel by Philip Roth (1983).

Books that mention bodies in their title include:
- *Bring Forth the Body*, by Simon Raven (1977), the ninth in the sequence called "Alms for Oblivion". The title is a quote from William Shakespeare's *Henry VI Part 1* (1590), "Bring forth the body of Sir John Salisbury" (2:ii:4).
- *The Body*, by William Sansom (1949), a disturbing study of obsessive jealousy.
- *The Body Servant*, by James Kirkup (1977). Poems of exile.
- *Written on the Body*, by Jeanette Winterson (1992), in which the loved one's body is described in anatomical and allegorical terms.

16 April: Hans Sloane (1660-1753) Physician, whose
library and natural history collection became the British Museum

FAMOUS LAST WORDS

"La Riviere" de Bailli
(French doctor; died 1605)
"I must hasten away since my baggage has been sent before me"

Albrecht von Haller
(German physician; died 1777)
He checked his own pulse … "Now I'm dying. The artery ceases to beat"

John Abernathy
(English surgeon, died 1831)
"Is there anyone in the room?"

Herman Boerhaave
(Dutch doctor; died 1738)
"He that loves God ought to think nothing desirable but what is pleasing to the Supreme Goodness"

Sir William Osler
(Regius Professor of Medicine, Oxford; died 1919)
"Nightie-night, a-darling"

Oliver Wendell Holmes
(Doctor and poet, died 1935)
Before he was put into an oxygen tent: "Lot of damn foolery"

Anton Chekhov
(Doctor and poet; died 1904)
"I'm dying. I haven't drunk champagne for a long time"

William Cullen
(Scottish physician; died 1790)
"I wish I had the power of writing for then I would describe to you how pleasant it is to die"

Sir Samuel Garth
(Physician and poet; died 1718)
"I'm going on a long journey. They have greased my boots already"

---

18 April: Humphrey Verdon Roe (1878-1949)
Founded the first birth-control clinic in Britain with his wife,
Marie Stopes

FAMOUS LAST WORDS (cont'd)

Elie Metchnikov
(Bacteriologist; died 1916)
"Do you remember your promise to do my post mortem? Examine the intestines carefully; I think there is something there"

Francois Rabelais
(Doctor and poet; died 1553)
"I have nothing. I owe much. The rest I leave to the poor"

BRADFORD HILL'S NINE CRITERIA

In 1965, in *"The Environment and Disease: Association or Causation"*, Sir Austin Bradford Hill outlined nine criteria that, if met, strengthen the leap from association to causation (but see Phillips & Goodman, *Epidemiol Perspect Innov* 2004; 1: 3).

Strength
The association is so strong that we can easily rule out other factors

Consistency
The results have been replicated by different researchers and under different conditions

Specificity
The exposure is associated with a very specific disease, as opposed to a wide range of diseases

Temporality
The exposure preceded the disease

Biological gradient (dose-responsiveness)
Increasing exposure is associated with increasing risk

Plausibility
There is a credible scientific mechanism to explain the association

Coherence
The association is consistent with the natural history of the disease

Experimental evidence
A physical intervention gives results consistent with the association

Analogy
There is a similar result to which we can adduce a relationship

---

22 April: Robert Bárány (1876-1936)
Physiology and pathology of the vestibular apparatus
of the ear, Nobel prize 1914

A COMIC MEDICAL ALPHABET

A for a disiac
B for blockers; B for variant CJD
C for lytic
D for Kate; D for ent ducts
E for anaesthesia; E for ent arterioles
F for vescent tablets; F for moterol
G for surgery (a US title)
H for scratching
I for thyroidism; I for mectin
J Forensic Sci
K for scoliosis; K for the community
L for interferon
M for zema; M for tericin B
N for a red; N for a mammary
O for ectomy; O for treatment
P for urinalysis
Q for cancer; Q for outpatients
R for tablet twice a day
S for gillus fumigatus
T for dentures
U for cough
V for voce examination
W for your fee (a dangerous gamble)
X for in vitro fertilisation
Y for job? (the doctor's dilemma)
Z for de doctor (I've got a code iddy doze)

SUICIDE IN OPERA: DROWNING

Snegurorochka/The Snow Maiden (Nikolai Rimsky-Korsakov, 1882)
Mizguir drowns himself in a lake after his beloved Snow Maiden is melted by sunlight after having fallen in love

Lady Macbeth of Mtsensk (Dmitry Shostakovich, 1934)
Katerina Ismailova drowns herself in a river in despair at being abandoned by her new husband Sergei on the way to a prison camp in Siberia

---

23 April: Johannes Andreas Grib Fibiger (1867-1928)
Discovery of the *Spiroptera* cancer, Nobel prize 1926

SHAKESPEARIAN DISEASES

Aguecheek's disease
Twelfth Night (1623)
Chronic hepatic encephalopathy

Falstaff obesity
Henry IV, Part I (1598); Henry IV, Part II (1600);
The Merry Wives of Windsor (1602)
Due to excessive consumption of food; related to Erysichthon syndrome

Hamlet-Gertrude complex
Hamlet (1603)
A repressed Oedipus complex; the son being attracted to the mother

Othello syndrome
Othello (1622)
Morbid jealousy

King Lear complex
King Lear (1608)
Lust of a father for his daughter

Ophelia complex
Hamlet (1603)
Suicide by drowning

Ophelia syndrome
Hamlet (1603)
Loss of memory in patients with Hodgkin's disease

Romeo error
Romeo and Juliet (1597)
Spontaneous revival after being certified as dead

UNSCIENTIFIC NAMES: SONIC HEDGEHOG

A signalling molecule that shapes the brain during development. Named after a character in a computer game.

---

1 May: Santiago Ramón y Cajal (1852-1934)
Structure of the nervous system, Nobel prize 1906

SOME DANGEROUS DRUGS

Several drugs have been withdrawn because of unwanted effects:

Drug	Year	Unwanted effect
Diododiethyl tin	1954	Cerebral oedema
Thalidomide	1961	Congenital malformations
Clioquinol	1975	Brain damage
Benoxaprofen	1982	Liver damage
Zimeldine	1983	Allergy
Fenclofenac	1984	Skin disease
Suprofen	1987	Kidney damage
Noscapine	1991	Genetic damage
Terodiline	1991	Heart arrhythmias
Triazolam	1991	Psychiatric disorders
Centoxin	1993	Increased mortality
Remoxipride	1994	Anaemia
Troglitazone	1997	Liver damage
Fenfluramine	1997	Heart valve damage
Tolcapone	1998	Liver damage
Astemizole	1998	Heart arrhythmias
Sertindole	1998	Heart arrhythmias
Cisapride	2003	Heart arrhythmias
Kava kava	2004	Liver damage
Rofecoxib	2004	Stroke

FAMOUS PHARMACISTS

Dante Alighieri
Benedict Arnold
Emil Coué
Benjamin Franklin
Johann Wolfgang von Goethe
O. Henry (William Sydney Porter)
Hubert Humphrey
Henrik Ibsen
Isaac Newton
Amerigo Vespucci

---

2 May: Benjamin Spock (1903-1998)
American paediatrician and author of the leading baby book
in the 1950s and 60s

EUPHEMISMS: DIARRHOEA

Adriatic tummy
Aztec hop
Back-door trot
Basra belly
Bechuana tummy
Cairo crud
Delhi belly
Edgar Brits
Flying handicap
Gastric flu
Gippy tummy
Hong Kong dog
Mexican toothache
Montezuma's revenge
Napoleon's revenge
Rangoon runs
Runny tummy
Runs
Scatters
Shits
Spanish tummy
Squits
Threepennies
Tokyo two-step
Turistas

CATCH PHRASES

Doctor Livingstone, I presume?
Is there a doctor in the house?
Just what the doctor ordered
My son the doctor
You're the doctor
Hello, baby! How's nurse?
Good night, nurse
Bring on the body

6 May: Sigmund Freud (1856-1939)
Austrian neurologist, invention of psychoanalysis

ROCK DOCS

Dr Alban
Nigerian male vocalist Albam Nwapa

Doctor and the Medics
UK male/female pop group

Dr Dre
US hiphop artist (né Andre Young)

Dr Feelgood
UK male/female pop group

Dr Fox
UK Capital radio disk jockey

Dr Hook
New Jersey pop duo

Dr Octagon
American pop music producer

Doctor Spin
UK male instrumental/production duo

MAXIMUM LONGEVITY OF VERTEBRATES (IN YEARS)

Marion's tortoise (*Testudo sumeiri*)	150+
Human (*Homo sapiens sapiens*)	120+
Galapagos tortoise (*Testudo elephantopus*)	100+
Elephant (*Elephas indicus*)	77
Horse (*Equus caballus*)	50
Rhinoceros (*Rhinoceros unicornis*)	49
Chimpanzee (*Pan troglodytes*)	39
Dog (*Canis familiaris*)	34
Cat (*Felis catus*)	31
Rabbit (*Oryctolagus cuniculus*)	14

8 May: André Michael Lwoff (1902-1994)
Microbial genetics, Nobel prize 1965

ABORTION

The term abortion is derived from the Latin *ab* (away from) and *oriri* (to be born). Strictly speaking, it refers to any type of abortion, both spontaneous and induced, and occurs before 28 weeks of pregnancy; delivery of a fetus after that and before full term is called premature delivery. However, spontaneous abortion is more usually called miscarriage. Induced abortion is usually procured nowadays by the use of a prostaglandin plus a progestogen, to stimulate uterine contraction, or by suction. The term "abortion pill" for an abortifacient was previously used to describe any substance that was used to procure an abortion, whether effective or not.

Ancient abortifacients included:

Aloes   Cantharides   Cottonwood   Dichylon   Ergot
Lead   Nutmeg (Myristica fragrans)   Pennyroyal   Quinine
Tansy   Veratrum (wild cucumber)   Zoapatle (Montana tomentosa)

TYPES OF SIAMESE TWINS

There are eight major types of Siamese twins, more properly called conjoined twins (*J Paediatr Surg* 1996; 31: 941-4):

Cephalopagus
Joined from the top of the head down to the umbilicus, with two faces
Thoracopagus
Joined face to face from the upper chest to the umbilicus
Omphalopagus
Joined face to face around the umbilicus
Ischiopagus
Joined face to face at the pelvis
Parapagus
Joined at the side to different extents
Craniopagus
Joined at any part of the skull except the face
Pygopagus
Joined back to back at the pelvis
Rachipagus
Joined back to back above the pelvis

---

11 May: Justus von Liebig (1803-73)
Discovery of chloroform

WELLERISMS

The term "wellerism" was used most likely for the first time in the *Boston Morning Globe* of 9 January 1839. Reminiscent of expressions used by Sam Weller and his father, Tony Weller, in Charles Dickens' *Pickwick Papers*, a "wellerism" consists of three parts:

1. A speech or statement (often a proverb)
2. Identification of the speaker
3. Identification of the circumstances, giving an ironic twist, often with a pun

An example of a wellerism is: "'Prevention is better than cure,' said the pig when it ran away from the butcher." Wellerisms containing medical and anatomical terms include:

"Too much bile in my stomach," as the teakettle said when hanging over a hot fire.

"I only assisted natur', ma'm," as the doctor said to the boy's mother, arter he'd bled him to death.

"Blood will tell," quoth Macbeth, as he tried to scrub it off.

"I shall make no bones about it, anyway," smiled the convicted murderer when he learned his body was to be burned in quick lime.

"That's an unkind cut," as the man said ven his razor slipt.

As the old beggarman said to his dame, "God send you your health as long as I live."

"I've got a hunch," said the dwarf, when the doctors asked him what his ailment was.

"Well, of all the nerve," murmured the lady dentist, as she investigated the molar.

"I'll spare no pains," as the quack said when he sawed off his patient's leg for rheumatism.

"We'll be all right now," said the doctor, "if we don't run out of patients."

---

13 May: Ronald Ross (1857-1932)
Discovery of the transmission of malaria, Nobel prize 1902

WELLERISMS (cont'd)

"You make me sick," said the man to the germ.

"That will be enough out of you," said the doctor, as he stitched the patient together.

"I'm not i' the vein," as the lancet said when the unskilled practitioner stuck it in the artery.

IRREVERENT ABBREVIATIONS

5H1T (cf. 5HT)	Merde
AGMI	Ain't Gonna Make It
BTSOOM	Beats The Shit Out Of Me
CRAFT	Can't Remember A Flipping Thing
ERCP	Emergency Retrograde Clerking of Patient
FUBAR BUNDY	Fouled Up Beyond All Recognition, But Unfortunately Not Dead Yet
GLM	Good Looking Mum
GOK	God Only Knows
GOMER	Get Out Of My Emergency Room
HTK	Higher Than a Kite
ITBNTL	In The Box, Nail The Lid
KFO	Knock the Fellow Out
LOBNH	Lights On But Nobody Home
MICO	Masterly Inactivity and Cat-like Observation
NKDA (Usually No Known Drug Allergy)	Not Known, Didn't Ask
O sign	Patient unconscious with mouth open
PAFO	Pissed And Fell Over
Q sign	Patient unconscious, mouth open, tongue hanging out
RT	Room Temperature (dead)
SWAG	Scientific Wild Ass Guess
TALOIA	There's A Lot Of It About
TUBE	Totally Unnecessary Breast Examination
UBI	Unexplained Beer Injury
VAC	Vultures Are Circling (dying)
YOYO	You're On Your Own

---

14 May: Gabriel Daniel Fahrenheit (1686-1736)
Invention of the mercury thermometer

DEDICATED TO DEDICATIONS

Aleister Crowley, *Diary of a Drug Fiend* (1922)
*To Alostrael, Virgin Guardian of the Sangraal in the Abbey of
Thelema in "Telepylus", and to Astarte, Lulu, Panthaea, its youngest member,
I dedicate this story of its Herculean labours towards releasing Mankind from
every form of bondage*

Leslie Fiedler, *Freaks* (1978)
To my brother who has no brother, to all my brothers who have no brother

William Harvey, *Movement of the Heart and Blood in Animals:
An Anatomical Essay (1628)*
*To the most serene and most puissant Charles [I], King of Great Britain,
France, and Ireland, Defender of the Faith...*

Dr David Livingstone, *Missionary Travels and Researches in South Africa*
(1857). *To Sir Roderick Impey Murchison, President of the Royal
Geographical Society, this work is affectionately offered as a token of
gratitude for the kind interest he has always taken in the Author's pursuits
and welfare; and to express admiration of his eminent scientific attainments,
nowhere more strongly evidenced than by the striking hypothesis respecting
the physical conformation of the African continent, promulgated in his
Presidential address to the Royal Geographical Society in 1852, and verified
three years afterwards by the Author of these travels.*

Betty Macdonald, *The Plague and I* (1948)
*For Dr Robert M Smith, Dr Clyde R Jensen, and Dr Bernard P Mullen,
without whose generous hearts and helping hands I would probably be just
another name on a tombstone*

Maurice H. Pappworth, *Human guinea pigs.
Experimentation on man* (1967)
*This book is dedicated to my four sources of inspiration, my wife Jean (Ayshet
Chayil - "a woman of worth"), and Joanna, Dinah and Sara, our delightful
daughters*

Alfred J. Sewell, *The Dog's Medical Dictionary (1906)*
*The reviser dedicates this book to PEB, who like himself wishes it to be a real
help to our friend the dog in his hour of need, and hopes it may prove a worthy
successor to the general work of his late partner*

> 15 May: Pierre Curie (1859-1906)
> Discovery of radium

ZZZZZZZZZZZ

Of the few drugs whose names begin with the letter zed, three are hypnotics. They are:

Zaleplon
Zolpidem
Zopiclone

They are collectively known as the Z's.

EUPHEMISMS: MENSTRUATION

Ammunition
Bad news
Buns on
Caller
Captain/cardinal is at home
Cramps
Feminine hygiene
My flag is up
My friend has come
Grandmother to stay
Have the painters in
Holy week
In purdah
Kit has come
Little visitor
Monthly flowers
Old faithful
Out of circulation
Pleasure-garden padlock
Rags on
(The) Red Sea is in
Redhaired visitor
Ride the red horse
Road is up for repair
So-so

16 May: Bernard Spilsbury (1877-1947)
British pathologist and expert witness in famous murder trials

OBESITY OBJECTIFIED

One commonly used tool for estimating weight status in adults is the Body Mass Index (BMI), originally known as Quetelet's index. It is calculated by dividing the weight of the patient (in kilograms) by the square of the patient's height (in metres), i.e. $weight/height^2$.

A simpler bedside approach is to use the Tupman scale, named in homage to the character in Charles Dickens's *Pickwick Club: Posthumous Papers:* "Time and feeding had expanded that once romantic form; the black silk waistcoat had become more and more developed; and gradually had the capacious chin encroached upon the borders of the white cravat."

For each level of fatness, subtract the indicated percentage from the total body weight to calculate the lean Tupman weight:

Pleasantly plump 5%
Portly 10%
Suety 15%
Tubby 20%
Rolypoly 25%
Blubbery 30%
Gross 35%
Indescribable 40%

Like other scales of this sort, such as the Beaufort scale of wind speeds (from calm to hurricane) or the Mohs scale of hardness (from talc to diamond), the Tupman scale is a touch impressionistic...

FAMOUS SUFFERERS: POLIO

Alan Alda   Arthur C. Clarke
Emperor Claudius   Mia Farrow
J. Robert Oppenheimer   Itzhak Perlman
Franklin Delano Roosevelt   Sir Walter Scott
Dinah Shore   Margarete Steiff   Ian Dury

17 May: Edward Jenner (1749-1823)
Invention of vaccination for smallpox

STRANGE DOCTORS

Never play cards with a man called Doc
(Nelson Algren, *Newsweek*, July 2, 1956)

Doc	One of the seven dwarves
Doctor Caligari	Evil magician and hypnotist, played by Werner Krauss, in the German horror movie *The Cabinet of Dr Caligari* (1919)
Dr Death	Media name for a real or sham doctor who kills elderly patients, e.g. Sydney Noble
Dr Dolittle	An "animal doctor" in stories by Hugh Lofting
Doctor Faustus	An ageing philosopher, who sells his soul to the devil in return for earthly pleasures
Doc Holliday	Dentist friend of Wyatt Earp
Dr Emmett Brown	Crazy scientist, played by Christopher Lloyd, in *Back to the Future* (1985) and sequels (?prequels)
Doctor Jekyll	The alter ego of Mr Hyde in the novel *Doctor Jekyll and Mr Hyde* by Robert Louis Stevenson (1886)
Doc Martens	Brand name of a type of shoe, Dr Klaus Martens, a podiatrist
Doctor Octopus	Spiderman's sworn enemy
"Papa Doc" Duvalier	François Duvalier (1907-1971), Haiti's infamous dictator, succeeded by his son Jean-Claude (or Baby Doc)
Dr Pepper	Wade Morrison named his soft drink after Kenneth Pepper, a Virginia pharmacist for whom he had worked
Dr Scholl	William "Billy" Scholl, a podiatrist from LaPorte, Indiana, USA
Doctor Seuss	Theodore Seuss Geisel, author of children's books
Dr Strangelove	Satirical film, starring Peter Sellers in three roles, about the threat of global nuclear destruction (1964)
Doctor Who	Time Lord who travels in the Tardis in children's science fiction TV series

---

22 May: Willem Einthoven (1860-1927)
Invention of the electrocardiograph, Nobel prize 1924

METALS IN MEDICINE

Bronze baby syndrome
Excessive ultraviolet radiation in a neonate with hepatocellular disease

Bronze diabetes
Haemochromatosis

Staphylococcus aureus
The colonies, when grown on solid media, are the colour of gold (Latin 'aureus')

Lead-pipe rigidity
One of the signs of Parkinson's disease

Lead-pipe colon
The result of advanced scarring in ulcerative colitis

Silver wiring
Hypertensive retinopathy

Sulphur granules
Seen in actinomycosis

FAMOUS SUFFERERS: EPILEPSY

Bud Abbott	*Alexander the Great*
Richard Burton	*George Gordon Byron*
Julius Caesar	*Truman Capote*
Lewis Carroll	*Dante Alighieri*
Charles Dickens	*Fyodor Dostoyevsky*
Gustave Flaubert	*Vincent Van Gogh*
Margaux Hemingway	*Soren Kierkegaard*
Edward Lear	*Teresa McLean*
Napoleon Bonaparte	*Edgar Allen Poe*
Sir Walter Scott	*Socrates*
Pyotr Illyich Tchaikovsky	*Alfred Lord Tennyson*

---

23 May: Joshua Lederberg (1925-)
Bacterial genetics, Nobel prize for discovery that genes act by
regulating definite chemical events 1958

Pieces of Prose: Nursing

*My three days' experiences had begun with a death, and, owing to the
defalcation of another nurse, a somewhat abrupt plunge into the
superintendence of a ward containing forty beds, where I spent my shining
hours washing faces, serving rations, giving medicine, and sitting in
a very hard chair, with pneumonia on one side, diphtheria on the other, two
typhoids opposite, and a dozen dilapidated patriots, hopping, lying, and
lounging about, all staring more or less at the new "nuss," who suffered
untold agonies, but concealed them under as matronly an aspect as a
spinster could assume, and blundered through her trying labors with a
Spartan firmness, which I hope they appreciated, but am afraid they
didn't. Having a taste for "ghastliness," I had rather longed for the wounded
to arrive, for rheumatism wasn't heroic, neither was liver complaint, or
measles; even fever had lost its charms since "bathing burning brows"
had been used up in romances, real and ideal. But when I peeped into the
dusky street lined with what I at first had innocently called market carts,
now unloading their sad freight at our door, I recalled sundry reminiscences
I had heard from nurses of longer standing, my ardor experienced a sudden
chill, and I indulged in a most unpatriotic wish that I was safe at home
again, with a quiet day before me, and no necessity for being hustled up,
as if I were a hen and had only to hop off my roost, give my plumage a
peck, and be ready for action.*

Extract from Louisa May Alcott,
Hospital Sketches and Camp and Fireside Stories (1863)

Louisa May Alcott volunteered to serve as a nurse at the Union Hotel Hospital,
Washington DC during the American Civil War, nursing the wounded from the
Battle of Fredericksburg. Only six weeks after having arrived in Washington,
Alcott fell ill with typhoid fever and was subsequently sent home. She was
treated with a mercury-based compound, but suffered the effects of mercury
poisoning for the rest of her life.

23 May: Franz Mesmer (1734-1815)
Invention of mesmerism

ORIGINS OF PHARMACEUTICAL COMPANIES

Most drug companies are named after their founders (e.g. PFIZER after Charles Pfizer); here are some with names of other origins:

CIBA
(Chemische Industrie Basel Aktiengesellschaft; Chemical Industries of Basel Company)
Founded in Basel, Switzerland in 1859. Name registered in 1904
Merged with J. R. Geigy in 1970 (CIBA-GEIGY)
In 1996, merged with Sandoz and name changed to
NOVARTIS *(signifying new art)*

GLAXO
Founded in 1873 in Wellington, New Zealand as Joseph Nathan and Company
In 1900, Nathan (who had emigrated from London in 1853)
bought a milk-drying process that he exported
He tried to register the company as Lacto, but this name was unacceptable to the registrar of companies
So he registered the name Glaxo (from the Greek word for milk, galax)

HOECHST
Founded in town Hoechst, west of Frankfurt, Germany, in 1863

MEDICAL STUDENTS WHO DID NOT GRADUATE

Giorgio Armani, designer
Lew Ayres (but later played Dr Kildare in a series of films)
Neil Diamond, pop star
Christopher Isherwood, author
Robin Givens, actress
Dustin Hoffman, actor
James Joyce, author
Bill Murray, actor
William Roach, actor (Ken Barlow in Coronation Street)
Wim Wenders, film director

---

26 May: William Petty (1623-87)
Invention of vital statistics

Pop and Rock Song Titles

Accident Prone	Status Quo
Accidents Will Happen	Elvis Costello
Adrenalin	N-Joi
Amnesia	Shalamar/Chumbawumba
Asshole	Dennis Leary
Bleed	Catatonia
Bloodshot Eyes	Millie
The Boy With The X-ray Eyes	Babylon Zoo
Brain	Jungle Brothers
Brain Stew	Green Day
Broken Nose	Catherine Wheel
Cardiac Arrest	Madness
Colourblind	Darius
The Drugs Don't Work	Verve
Emergency (Dial 999)	Loose Ends
Fever	Peggy Lee/Madonna/Starsailor
Frontier Psychiatrist	The Avalanches
The Gentle Art Of Choking	My Vitriol
Heart Attack	Olivia Newton John
Heart Attack And Vine	Screaming Jay Hawkins
Hotel Illness	The Black Crowes
Injected With A Poison	Praga Khan
Jungle Fever	Chakachas
Kiss Like Ether	Claudia Brucken
Legs	ZZ Top
Let The Healing Begin	Joe Cocker
Madness (Is All In The Mind)	Madness
My Iron Lung	Radiohead
NHS (EP)	DJ Doc Scott
Night Nurse	Sly and Robbie featuring Simply Red
Novocaine For the Soul	Eels
Oxygen	Blaggers I.T.A/JJ72
Paralyzed	Elvis Presley
Pregnant For The Last Time	Morrissey
Scar Tissue	Red Hot Chili Peppers
Skeletons	Stevie Wonder
Tourniquet	Marilyn Manson/Headswim
Tranquillizer	Geneva
X Ray Follow Me	Space Frog

---

28 May: Joseph Guillotin (1738-1814)
Proponent of the guillotine

GP GEOGRAPHY

Australia antigen *Surface antigen on Hepatitis B virus, first described in an Australian patient by Baruch S Blumberg*

Baghdad boil *Cutaneous leishmaniasis (also known as* **Oriental sore***)*

Bairnsdale ulcer *Skin ulcer due to Mycobacterium ulcerans; town in Victoria, Australia (also called* **Buruli lesion** *after Buruli, Africa near the Nile river)*

Balkan nephropathy *Interstitial nephritis of unknown cause occurring around the Balkan area*

Bornholm disease *Epidemic pleurodynia due to Coxsackie B virus; town in New York State, USA*

Devonshire colic *Lead poisoning, first described by Sir George Baker in Devon*

Ebola virus *Haemorrhagic fever; river in the Democratic Republic of Congo*

German measles *Alternative name for rubella viral illness*

Haff disease *Acute rhabdomyolysis secondary to ingesting certain fish e.g. buffalo fish; named after a harbour (German haff) in which the fish swim*

Japanese encephalitis *Neurological viral infection spread by mosquitoes; closely related to* **St Louis encephalitis** *and* **West Nile virus**

Lassa fever *Viral infection carried by rodents; Lassa township is in North-Eastern Nigeria*

Lyme disease *Tick-borne infection; Old Lyme, Connecticut*

Malta fever *Alternative name for brucellosis*

Marburg fever *African haemorrhagic fever, first brought over from Uganda into Marburg, Germany in African green monkeys imported for research*

Minamata disease *Mercury poisoning from eating contaminated shellfish; first described after the Chisso Corporation dumped mercury compounds into Minamata Bay in Japan*

New Guinea lung *Extrinsic allergic alveolitis due to mouldy dust from thatched roofs*

Norwalk agent *Viral gastroenteritis first reported in Norwalk, Ohio*

Norwegian scabies *Form of scabies with heavy infestation of mites; first described in Norway as a form of leprosy*

---

30 May: Julius Axelrod (1912-1983)
Work on sympathetic neurotransmitters, Nobel prize 1970

Oroya fever	*Acute febrile phase of Carrion's disease (bartonellosis); La Oroya is a town in the foothills of the Peruvian Andes*
Plaster of Paris	*First mined from a large gypsum deposit at Montmartre in Paris, France; Paris, a town in Ontario, is so named as this was the raw material used for many of its early buildings*
Pontiac fever	*Milder form of legionellosis than Legionnaire disease; described after outbreak in 1968 in Pontiac, Michigan*
Rift Valley fever	*Acute febrile viral disease; fissure stretching through Kenya*
San Joaquin Valley fever	*Coccidioidomycosis; valley in Southern California, USA*
Siamese twins	*Now properly known as conjoined twins; named after Chang and Eng Bunker, born in Siam (now Thailand) to Chinese parents*

ETYMOLOGY: COUGH

Cough, pronounced coff, is onomatopoeic in origin, from the sound of the closure of the glottis plus the sound of air whizzing or wheezing through the trachea. Other languages have different ways of mimicking the sound of a cough. The Greek word was bex, with its guttural stem bekh-. The Latin word was tussis, with its own form of onomatopoeia, giving modern words like toux (French), tosse (Italian and Portuguese), and toz (Spanish).

However, more northerly languages have Husten (German), hoost (Dutch), hoste (Danish), and hosta (Swedish), which sound like a cough without the initial closure of the glottis, more like what we call huffing, as in huffing and puffing (which nowadays means objecting loudly). According to Lewis Carroll, uffish, a nonsense word that he used in Jabberwocky, reflected a state of mind in which "the voice is gruffish, the manner roughish, and the temper huffish." And among drug users, to huff means to inhale, usually in reference to marijuana.

Finally, coughing and huffing come together in the German word for whooping cough, Keuchhusten.

---

2 June: Jesse Boot (1850-1931)
Pharmacist and founder of Boots The Chemist

MELLOW YELLOW

The Ancient Greeks had several words for yellow, including xanthos, ochros, and chloros, none of which was the colour that we call yellow today. Xanthos was a kind of bay colour, like that of the horse of that name, and ochros was a very pale yellow, like the colour of sand. Chloros was closer to green than yellow.

Xanthochromia
This refers to the yellow discolouration of cerebrospinal fluid,
often as a result of a subarachnoid haemorrhage (a cause of stroke)
with subsequent haemoglobin breakdown

Xanthines (derivatives of xanthic acid)
e.g. caffeine and theophylline (the latter is used in the treatment of asthma)
Xanthines leave a lemon yellow residue when reacted with nitric acid

Xanthoastrocytoma
A type of brain tumour that appears yellow due to high lipid content

Xanthopsia
A visual defect in which objects have a yellowish hue;
known effect of digitalis toxicity
*Vincent van Gogh may have suffered from xanthopsia as a result of
digitalis therapy (extracted from the purple foxglove plant) for mania
and/or epilepsy prescribed by his physician Dr Paul-Ferdinand Gachet of
Auvers-sur-Oise. He was certainly fond of yellow, as witnessed by the
yellow tinting of many of his paintings, such as The Starry Night,
Sunflowers, and Yellow Chair with Pipe. M. Albert-Puleo put forward an
alternative theory, that van Gogh was suffering from the hallucinogenic
effects of absinthe, or wormwood, from Artemisia absinthum.*

Xanthomata and xanthelasmata
Irregular yellow skin patches associated with raised blood lipids

Ochronosis
A yellow-brown discolouration of certain tissues of the body,
notably cartilage, associated with alkaptonuria, due to an inborn
error of metabolism

---

3 June: Otto Loewi (1873-1961)
Discovery of chemical transmission in neurons, Nobel prize 1936

Pieces of Poetry: Alcohol

What is strong drink? Let me think - I answer 'tis a thing
From whence the majority of evils spring,
And causes many a fireside with boisterous talk to ring,
And leaves behind it a deadly sting...

Strong drink to the body can do no good;
It defiles the body, likewise the food,
And causes the drunkard with pain to groan,
Because it extracts the marrow from the bone:

And hastens him on to a premature grave,
Because to the cup he is bound a slave;
For the temptation is hard to thole,
And by it he will lose his immortal soul.

Extract from William McGonagall,
A Tribute to Mr Murphy and the Blue Ribbon Army (1890)

Some Famous Dentists

Dr GWA Bonwill	*Developer of the modern safety pin*
Doc Holliday	*Fought at the OK Corral with the Earp brothers*
Dr Pearl Zane Grey	*Author of western novels as Zane Grey*
Mahloon Loomis	*Original inventor of wireless telegraphy before Marconi but unrecognized due to lack of financial backing*
Dr William Lovell	*Inventor of the wooden golf tee*
Paul Revere	*Folk hero of the American Revolution, immortalised in a poem by Henry Wadsworth Longfellow (and in a rap song by The Beastie Boys)*
William F Semple	*Added sugar and flavourings to chicle to make chewing gum in 1869*
Charles R Stent	*Invented a type of material for taking dental impressions, later used to mould body cavities; hence, a tube used to keep a vessel open*
Dr Thomas Welch	*Developed Welch's grape juice*

5 June: Allvar Gullstrand (1862-1930)
Work on the dioptrics of the eye, Nobel prize 1908

Conditions Seen in Paintings

Albinism
Nude Girl on a Fur (1932)
Otto Dix

Blindness
Parable of the Blind (1568)
Pieter Brueghel

Clubfoot
The Clubfooted Boy (1642)
Jusepe de Ribera

Congenital heart disease (Fallot's tetralogy?)
Any self-portrait
Dick Ket

Dupuytren's contracture
Portrait of Fridel Battenberg (1920)
Max Beckmann

Epidermolysis bullosa
Heritage (1899)
Edvard Munch

Mental disease
The Cure for Folly (c 1480)
Hieronymus Bosch

Phocomelia
Mother with Deformed Infant (c 1805)
Francisco de Goya

Pyknodysostosis
Any self-portrait
Henri de Toulouse-Lautrec

Spastic paraplegia
Child on All Fours (after Muybridge) (1961)
Francis Bacon

---

8 June: Francis Crick (1916-2004)
Discovery of the structure of DNA, Nobel prize 1962

CONDITIONS SEEN IN PAINTINGS (cont'd)

Strabismus
Any self-portrait
Albrecht Dürer

RIOTOUSLY RED

Of all the Greek words for red, only erythros has made it etymologically into English. Others were pyrsos, miltopreptos (crimson), halourges, and phoinikos. The Latin word was rubeus.

Erythema
Redness of the skin

Erysipelas
Red inflammation of skin, usually of the face, due to infection with a streptococcus

Erythrocyte
A red blood cell

Erythropoietin
A hormone, produced in the kidney that stimulates the bone marrow to produce red blood cells

Erythromelalgia
Dilatation of the blood vessels in the hands and feet, making them burn painfully

Rubefacient
Something (like alcohol) that you rub on the skin to encourage vasodilatation, turning it red

Rubeola and rubella
Measles and German measles

Kwashiorkor
Protein deficiency, which causes the skin and hair to turn a golden-red colour (Ghanaian for "red boy")

9 June: Elizabeth Garrett Anderson (1836-1917)
The first British woman to qualify as a doctor

THREE ASTOUNDING ACRONYMS

Nystatin
*New York State
Institute*

Warfarin
*Wisconsin Alumni
Research Foundation*

Eusol
*Edinburgh University
Solution*

COCKNEY RHYMING SLANG

Almond (rock)	Penis (cock)
Apple/scarlet/sherry pips	Lips
Bacon and eggs	Legs
Ball of lead	Head
Band in the box/Coachman on the box	Syphilis (pox)
Bang and biff	Syphilis (syph or siff)
Beatties and Babs	Crablice (crabs)
Beecham's Pills	Testicles
Beef-heart	Fart
Big Bloke	Cocaine (coke)
Big hit	To defaecate (shit)
Biscuits and cheese	Knees
Boat race	Face
Bottle and glass	Arse
Bread and cheese	Sneeze
Bristol City	Breast (titty)
Cat and kitties	Breasts (titties)
Chalk Farm	Arm
Cheltenham bold	Cold
Colleen Bawn	Erection (horn)
Conan Doyle	Boil
Elephant and Castle	Anus (arsehole)
Giggle stick	Penis (prick)
Gregory Peck	Neck
Gungah Din/Erroll Flynn	Chin
Hat and cap/Horse and trap	Gonorrhoea (clap)
Hampstead Heath	Teeth
J Arthur (Rank)	Masturbation (wank)
Jimmy Brits	Diarrhoea (shits)
Jimmy Riddle	To urinate (piddle)
Jumping Jack	Back
Khyber Pass	Anus (arse)

---

12 June: Fritz Albert Lipmann (1899-1986)
Discovery of coenzyme A, Nobel prize 1953

COCKNEY RHYMING SLANG (cont'd)

Levy and Frank	Masturbation (wank)
Maria Monk	Sperm (spunk)
Mutt and Jeff	Deaf
Ruby rose/I suppose	Nose
Salmon and trout	Mouth/gout/snout
Sighs and tears/King Lears	Ears
Steak and kidney/mince pie	Eye
Very best	Chest
You know	Cocaine (snow)

TRUE BLUE

In Greek the word for blue was kyanos. The Latin words were caeruleus and azura, from Arabic al and Persian lajward.

Cyanosis
A blue colouring of the skin and mucous membranes (e.g. of the lips and tongue) due to absence of oxygen from either the blood (central cyanosis) or the tissues (peripheral cyanosis)

Cyanhaemoglobin
A form of haemoglobin formed by reaction with hydrocyanic acid. But it makes the blood bright red!

Cyanocobalamin
A form of vitamin B_{12}

Cyanopsia
A form of abnormal colour vision in which everything appears blue; occurs rarely in digitalis intoxication

Caeruloplasmin
A globulin that carries 96% of the copper that circulates in the blood

Azurophilia
A condition in which blue-staining cells appear in the blood

---

13 June: Jules Bordet (1870-1961)
Bacteriologist, Nobel prize for discoveries in immunity 1919

COLLECTIVE CARERS

A hive of allergologists
A bag of anaesthetists
A nucleus of neurosurgeons
A corps of anatomists
A colony of bacteriologists
A chamber of cardiologists
A manipulation of chiropracters
An interaction of clinical pharmacologists
A brace of dentists
A rash of dermatologists
A plague of epidemiologists
A movement of gastroenterologists
A family of general practitioners
A smear of gynaecologists
A clot of haematologists
A triad of hepatologists
A batch of immunologists
An infusion of interns
A gargle of laryngologists
A handful of mammologists
A relay of neurologists
A dearth of nurses
A section of obstetricians
A lump of oncologists
Lashings of ophthalmologists
A cast of orthopaedic surgeons
A column of osteopaths
A herd of otologists
A host of parasitologists
A body of pathologists
A mixture of pharmacists
A stretch of physiotherapists
A pile of proctologists
A couch of psychoanalysts
A complex of psychologists
A series of radiologists
A joint of rheumatologists
A slice of surgeons
A flood of urologists

14 June: Karl Landsteiner (1868-1943)
Discovery of blood groups, Nobel prize 1930

EUPHEMISMS: MALE GENITALIA

Aaron's rod
Acorns
Adams' arsenal
Balls
Big Steve
Bollocks
Chopper
Cobblers
Cojones
Crown jewels
Ding-a-ling
Down below
Essentials
Family jewels
Fun stick
General Custer
Giggle stick
Goolies
John Thomas
Joystick
Lunchbox
Manhood
Marbles
Meat and two veg
Member
Nuts
Pecker
Percy
Prick
Roger
Sausage
Serpent
Shaft
Tadger
Third leg
Vitals
Weapon
Willy

15 June: Thomas Huckle Weller (1915-)
Virologist, Nobel prize for work on polio 1954

LITERARY LURGIES

Alice in Wonderland experience
*Contraction and expansion of a pituitary tumour when the
patient is treated with an ergot alkaloid with dopamine agonist activity*

Alice in Wonderland syndrome
*Syndrome of bizarre distortions of own body image in some people
with migraine or epilepsy; also distortion in perception of sizes, shapes, and
spatial relations of objects in children with infectious mononucleosis*

Huckleberry Finn syndrome
Persistent truancy; from the book by Mark Twain

Jekyll and Hyde syndrome
*Repeated deterioration of elderly patients on discharge with improvement of
symptoms on readmission; from the book by Robert Louis Stevenson*

Lilliputian hallucination
*Hallucination where objects and people appear diminutive; from the book
Gulliver's Travels by Jonathan Swift*

Oblomov syndrome
*Preference for remaining in bed; from the book by Ivan Alexandrovich
Goncharov (1859), adapted as a play by Spike Milligan*

Peter Pan and Wendy syndrome
*An unfaithful husband and a long-suffering wife; from the book and play by
J M Barrie*

Pied Piper phenomenon
*The enticement of children away from society by a charismatic character, e.g.
Hitler youth; from the legend and the poem by Robert Browning*

Pinocchio appearance
*Haemangioma on the tip of the nose;
from the book by Carlo Collodi entitled Storia di
un burattino or Le avventure di Pinocchio*

Polyanna posture
Excessive optimism; from the book by Eleanor H. Porter

17 June: François Jacob (1920-)
Nobel prize for bacterial and viral genetics 1965

LITERARY LURGIES (cont'd)

Rip van Winkle syndrome
Hypersomnia; novella by Washington Irving (pseudonym Knickerbocker)

Shandy syndrome
Accidental compressive trauma to the penis; book by Laurence Sterne

Walter Mitty syndrome
Daydreaming; The Secret Life of Walter Mitty, story by James Thurber

ANATOMICALLY ENTITLED:
MOUTH AND TEETH

Dentologia
A poem about "the diseases of the teeth and their remedies"
by Solyman Brown (1840)

The Poor Mouth
Novel by Flann O'Brien, a near-anagrammatic pseudonym
of Brian O'Nolan (1941)

The Skin of Our Teeth
A play by Thornton Wilder (1942). "My bone cleaveth to my skin and to my
flesh, and I am escaped with the skin of my teeth." (Job 19:20)

The Horse's Mouth
A novel by Joyce Cary (1944), filmed by Ronald Neame in 1958; Alec Guinness
wrote the screenplay and starred as Gulley Jimson, a fictional amalgamation of
William Blake and Stanley Spencer

Deep Throat
A pornographic film (1972), in which Linda Lovelace
practised an unusual form of fellatio

Jaws
A novel by Peter Benchley (1974), made into a film by Steven
Spielberg in 1975, starring Robert Shaw, Roy Schneider, and Richard Dreyfuss;
it had three superfluous sequels, Jaws 2 (1978), Jaws 3-D (1983), and Jaws:
The Revenge (1987)

---

18 June: Charles Louis Alphonse Laveran (1845-1922)
Work on protozoa, Nobel prize 1907

HOSPITAL MOTTOES

FLECTA NON RESILIET
Bent but shall not spring back
Birmingham General Hospital, Birmingham

CHARITY UNIVERSAL
Bristol Royal Hospital, Bristol

DARE QUAM ACCIPERE
[It is better] to give than to receive (*Acts*, Chapter 20)
Guys Hospital, London (c 1709)

HOMO SUM; HUMANI NIHIL A ME ALIENUM PUTO
I am a man; I think nothing human alien to myself (Terence, Heauton
Timeroumenos, The Self-Tormentor)
The London Hospital, London

MISERIS SUCCURRERE DISCO
I learn how to help the wretched
The Middlesex Hospital, London

FIAT LUX
Let there be light (*Genesis*, Chapter 1)
Moorfields Eye Hospital, London

DEO DANTE DAMUS
God gives to us that we may give unto others
Robert Jones and Agnes Hunt Orthopaedic Hospital, Oswestry, Shropshire

VIRTUTE FIDEQUE
By virtue and faith
Royal Free Hospital School of Medicine, London

LABOR OMNIA VINCIT
Labour conquers all things (Virgil, *Georgics*, Book 1)
Royal Marsden Hospital, London

AUDIENT SURDI MULTIQUE LOQUENTUR
The deaf shall hear and many shall speak
Royal National Throat, Nose and Ear Hospital, London

---

19 June: Ernst Boris Chain (1906-79)
Isolation of penicillin, Nobel prize 1945

HOSPITAL MOTTOES (cont'd)

DEUS INCUBAT ANGUI
God lies on the snake (Publius Papinius Statius, *Silvae*, Book III)
St George's Hospital, London

RATIONE DIRIGE CURSUM
Use reason to guide your course
University College Hospital, London

ODYSSEUS AND ULYSSES

Homer tells in Book XIX of the Odyssey that the name Odysseus comes from odussomai, I hate, since his grandfather Autolycus prophesied that he would be hated by gods and men. In *The Greek Myths* Robert Graves suggested that the Latin version, Ulysses, came from the Greek words oulos (a wound) and ischea (the thigh), from the wound that Odysseus received from a boar as a young man.

Ulysses complex
"A son's reciprocal search for his estranged father to recomplete the trinity of relationships with his mother" (Am Imago 1971 Summer; 28(2): 158-86)

Ulysses contract
In order to pass the sirens Odysseus had himself tied to the mast while his crew plugged their ears with wax. Driven mad by the sirens' singing, Odysseus begged his men to release him, but they rowed on regardless. The sirens drowned themselves in chagrin at his escape. The Ulysses contract "permit[s] mental patients with recurrent treatable disorders to consent in advance to treatment which they might reject at a time when their cognitive abilities are impaired"
(Hastings Cent Rep. 1984; 14(3): 13-6)

Ulysses syndrome
The misinterpretation of false positive laboratory tests, leading to further investigations, which do not confer benefit and may even cause harm (Can Med Assoc J 1972; 106(2): 122-3). "An errant patient with a conundrum of symptoms but without an explanation for them might have to take iatrogenic detours only to learn after what are at times ulyssean vagaries that the initial diagnosis ... is in the end untenable" (J Lab Clin Med 2004; 144(1): 7-10)

---

20 June: Frederick Gowland Hopkins (1861-1947)
Discovery of vitamins

HISTORIC HERBALS

Theophrastus of Eresos, *Historia Plantarum* (4th Century BC)
Crateuas, *Unnamed Herbal* (2nd Century BC)
Nikander, *Alexipharmaka* (2nd Century BC)
Dioscorides, *De Materia Medica* (1st Century AD)
Apuleius Platonicus, *Herbarium* (5th Century AD)
Serapion the Younger, *Herbolario Volgare* (1390-1400)
Johannes Platearius, *Liber de Simplici Medicina* (14th Century AD)
Benedetto Rinio, *Liber de Simplicibus* (1419)
Hieronymus Bock, *New Kreutter Buch* (1539)
Leonhardt Fuchs, *De Historia Stirpium* (1542)
Rembert Dodoens, *Stirpium Historiae Pemptades* (1554)
The Badianus Herbal (1552); compiled by two Aztecs
Pier Antonio Michiel, *Cinquelibri di Piante* (16th Century AD)
John Gerard, *The Herball or Generall Historie of Plantes* (1633)
John Parkinson, *Theatrum Botanicum; The Theater of Plants* (1640)
Nicholas Culpeper, *The Complete Herbal And English Physician* (1653)
John Ray, *Historia Plantarum* (1686)
J. P. Tournefort, *Elemens de Botanique* (1694)
William Salmon, *Botanologia: The English Herbal* (1710)
Elizabeth Blackwell, *A Curious Herbal* (1736-9)
William Curtis, *Flora Londinensis* (1777)
P. Bulliard, *Herbieres de la France* (1780-1793)
Mrs M Grieve, *A Modern Herbal* (1931)

CLASSICS: DE MEDICINA

Written by Celsus (fl. 14-37 AD), the eight volumes of *De Medicina* were a part
of a larger encyclopaedia. It was among the first medical texts to be published by
the printing press in 1478. Many of the practices were used up till the 19th
century. Celsus was the first to describe heat, pain, redness, and swelling as the
four cardinal signs of inflammation. Topics covered in *De Medicina* were as
diverse as the history of medicine, diet and regimen, fevers, ulcers, venereal disease, facial plastic surgery using skin transplants, antiseptics, eye surgery, surgical hygiene, heart disease, the use of ligatures to stop arterial haemorrhage,
insanity, hydrotherapy, tonsillectomy, oral and dental surgery, and the removal
of bladder stones.

---

22 June: Julian Huxley (1887-1975)
English biologist, promoter of evolutionary theory

SPOONERISMS

Based on the utterings of Reverend William Archibald Spooner (1844-1930), Warden of New College, Oxford, these are forms of metatheses consisting of transposition of the initial or vowel sound of words, forming ridiculous sounding combinations.

Examples, supposedly from the horse's mouth include, "Will nobody pat my hiccup?" (on dropping his hat), "You have tasted two worms", and "Cinquering Kongs their titles take" (announcing the hymn in church).

Some medical examples include:

Know your blows
Rental deceptionist
Bottle in front of me
My zips are lipped
Sealing the hick
I hit my bunny phone
No tails

SHORT-SIGHTED ARTISTS

Georges Braque
Paul Cezanne
Hilaire-Germain-Edgar Degas (at least in one eye)
Andre Derain
Raoul Dufy
Holman Hunt
Oskar Kokoschka
Jan Matejko
Henri Matisse
Pierre-Auguste Renoir
Dunoyer de Segonzac
Max Slevogt
Henri de Toulouse-Lautrec
Camille Pisarro
Auguste Rodin
Jan Van Eyck
Vincent Van Gogh
Jan Van Delft Vermeer

---

23 June: Alfred Kinsey (1894-1956)
American sexologist

92

CURIOUS LITERARY DEATHS

Aretino, Pietro (1492-1557). *Italian satirist and salacious poet.* He laughed so heartily at an obscene adventure of his sisters that he fell off his stool and struck his head with sufficient force to kill himself.

Bennett, (Enoch) Arnold (1867-1931). *English novelist.* Died from typhoid after drinking water from a carafe in a Paris hotel, trying to demonstrate that the local water was safe.

Brooke, Rupert Chawner (1887-1915). *English poet.* Died on a French ship of septicaemia as a result of an infected mosquito bite aggravated by sunstroke. He had been on his way to fight in the World War I Dardanelles campaign, and was buried on the island of Skyros.

Byron, Lord George Gordon (1788-1824). *English poet.* Fell ill in April 1824 with marsh fever (malaria) after rowing a boat across a lagoon in a thunderstorm in Missolonghi and died as a result. He may well have also had an epileptic fit three months earlier.

Greene, Robert (1558-1592). *English dramatist.* Died after an excess of Rhenish wine and pickled herrings at a banquet of authors.

Johnson, Lionel Pigot (1867-1902). *English poet and critic.* Fell in Fleet Street off a bar stool after having too much to drink, and fractured his skull.

Wilde, Oscar Fingall O'Flahertie Wills (1854-1900). *Irish playwright, novelist, essayist, poet, and wit.* Died as a result of complications of middle ear disease while living in France under the assumed name of Sebastian Melmoth.

FAMOUS DEATHS: AIDS

*Arthur Ashe   Allan Bloom   Gia Carangi
Cyril Collard   Eazy-E
John C Holmes   Rock Hudson   Derek Jarman
Robert Mapplethorpe   Freddie Mercury
Anthony Perkins   Robert Reed, actor*

27 June: Hans Spemann (1869-1941)
Organization in embryonic development, Nobel prize 1935

CLASSICS: THE ANATOMIST

A play about the body snatchers William Burke (1792-1829) and William Hare (1790-1860), who supplied cadavers to the Scottish anatomist Robert Knox (1791-1862). The play was written by the Scottish doctor James Bridie (1930), whose real name was Osborne Henry Mavor. He also wrote *The Sleeping Clergyman*.

The exploits of Burke and Hare are also remembered in a children's nursery rhyme:

> *Up the close and down the stair*
> *In the house with Burke and Hare*
> *Burke's the butcher, Hare's the thief,*
> *Knox, the boy who buys the beef*

BEDSIDE LIBRARY FOR MEDICAL STUDENTS (SIR WILLIAM OSLER)

A liberal education may be had at a very slight cost of time and money. Well filled though the day be with appointed tasks, to make the best possible use of your one or of your ten talents, rest not satisfied with this professional training, but try to get the education if not of a scholar, at least of a gentleman. Before going to sleep read for half an hour, and in the morning have a book open on your dressing table. You will be surprised to find how much can be accomplished in the course of a year. I have put down a list of ten books which you may make close friends. There are many others; studied carefully these will help in the inner education of which I speak.

> *Old and New Testament*
> *Shakespeare*
> *Montaigne*
> *Plutarch's Lives*
> *Marcus Aurelius*
> *Epictetus*
> *Religio Medici*
> *Don Quixote*
> *Emerson*
> *Oliver Wendell Holmes Breakfast-Table Series*

---

28 June: Alexis Carrel (1873-1944)
Transplant surgeon, Nobel prize for work on vascular suture and the transplantation of blood vessels and organs 1912

Misinterpreted Meanings

Benign
What you do after you be eight

Cauterize
Made eye contact with her

Dilater
To live longer

Morbid
A higher offer

Nitrate
Lower than the day rate

Outpatient
A patient who has fainted

Prostate
Flat on your back

Protein
In favour of young people

Rectum
Dam' near killed 'em

Seizure
Roman emperor

Tumour
An extra pair

Varicose
Near by

Vein
Conceited

Anagrammatic Drugs

Anagrammatic beta-blockers

- *Alderlin (ICI's first beta-blocker - pronethalol)* Named after Alderley Edge, the lake near Manchester on which the headquarters of ICI sat.
- *Inderal (propranolol)* Introduced after Alderlin was withdrawn because of unwanted side effects.
- *Eraldin (practolol)* An anagram of Inderal.

And beta-blockers help you to solve anagrams more quickly (*Neuroreport* 2002; 13: 2505-7)

Anagrammatic vitamins

Pantothenic acid   Hopantenic acid

29 June: William James Mayo (1861-1939)
Co-founder of the Mayo clinic

An Alternative History of Medicine

"Doctor, doctor, my throat hurts…"

2000 BC
Here, eat this root
    1000 AD
    That root is heathen; here, say this prayer
        1850 AD
        That prayer is superstition; here, drink this potion
            1950 AD
            That potion is snake oil; here, swallow this pill
                1990 AD
                That pill is ineffective; here, take this antibody
                    2005 AD
                    That antibody is artificial; here, eat this root

Droll Drinking

Man, being reasonable, must get drunk;
The best of life is but intoxication:
Glory, the grape, love, gold, in these are sunk
The hopes of all men, and of every nation;
Without their sap, how branchless were the trunk
Of Life's strange tree, so fruitful on occasion:
But to return – get very drunk, and when
You wake with headache, you shall see what then.
Lord Byron, *Don Juan*

If merely "feeling good" could decide, drunkenness would be the supremely valid human experience
William James, *Varieties of Religious Experience*

We drink one another's health and spoil our own
Jerome K Jerome, *Idle Thoughts of an Idle Fellow*

There are two reasons for drinking: one is, when you are thirsty, to cure it; the other, when you are not thirsty, to prevent it
Thomas Love Peacock, *Melincourt*

---

30 June: Frederick Gowland Hopkins (1861-1947)
Discovery of vitamins, Nobel prize 1929

SEX MANUALS THROUGH THE AGES

Jules Guyot, *Breviar de L'amour Experimentale* (1859)
Dr Elizabeth Blackwell, *The Human Element in Sex* (1884)
G. H. Darwin, *Leuchorroea, or the Whites* (1884)
Ellis Ethelmer, *Phases of Love: As it Was; As it Is; As it Maybe* (1897)
Emma Angell Drake, *What a Young Wife Ought to Know* (1901)
Mary Ware Dennet, *The Sex Side of Life: An Explanation for Young People*
(1918)
Havelock Ellis, *On Life and Sex* (1920)
Rev The Hon E. Littleton, *Training of the Young in Laws of Sex* (1928)
Dr M. J. Exner, *The Sexual Side of Marriage* (1932)
Dr Eustace Chesser, *Love without fear: A plain guide to sex technique for every*
married adult (1941)
Edward Griffith, *Sex and Citizenship* (1941)
Leonora Eyles, *Sex for the Engaged* (1952)
Lucia Radl, *Illustrated Guide to Sex Happiness in Marriage* (1953)
Gilbert Oakley, *Sane and Sensual Sex* (1963)
Marie Stopes, *Married Life; A New Contribution to Sex Difficulties* (1963)
Alex Comfort, *The Joy of Sex* (1972)
Alex Comfort, *More Joy of Sex* (1975)
Gabrielle Brown, *The New Celibacy: How to Take a Vacation from Sex and*
Enjoy It (1980)
Helen Gurley Brown, *Having it All* (1982)
Philip Cauthery and Drs Andrew and Penny Stanway, *The Complete Book of*
Love and Sex: A Guide for All The Family (1983)
Sheila Kitzinger, *Woman's Experience of Sex* (1983)

LITERARY DOCTORS: NON-BRITISH

André Breton (1896-1966)
Mikhail Bulgakov (1891-1940)
Louis-Ferdinand Céline (1894-1961)
Anton Chekhov (1860-1904)
Arthur Schnitzler (1862-1931)
François Rabelais (1490-1553)
Friedrich von Schiller (1759-1805)

---

1 July: Gerald Maurice Edelman (1929-1983)
Chemical structure of antibodies, Nobel prize 1972

SIAMESE ANIMALS

Ancient myths of two-headed monsters from all over the world testify to the antiquity of conjoined twins. Here are some examples:

- *Aker* an Egyptian earth-god, a lion with a human head at each end.
- *Amphisbaena* a snake with a head at each end, described by Alexander Pope in the Dunciad.

  > "Thus Amphisbæna (I have read)
  > At either end assails;
  > None knows which leads, or which is led,
  > For both Heads are but Tails."

- *Hiyakudori* a Japanese two-headed bird, an emblem of perfect love, embodying as it does the souls of two lovers.
- *Janus* the two-faced Roman god of beginnings and doors.
- *Orthrus or Orthos* Geryon's two-headed dog, the brother of the three-headed dog Cerberus, offspring of Typhon and Echidna.
- *Sisiutl* a poisonous two-headed snake that could turn into a fish (Pacific Coast Indian myth).

And in fiction:

- *Pushmi-pullyu* A two-headed llama-like creature given by the monkeys to Dr Dolittle (*The Story of Doctor Dolittle*, Hugh Lofting, 1920). The animal had one head at each end of its body, and only one head slept at a time, so that it could always see where you were coming from.
- *Zaphod Beeblebrox*, President of the Galaxy.

  > "Arthur followed him in nervously and was astonished to see a man lolling back in a chair with his feet on a control console picking the teeth in his right-hand head with his left hand. The right-hand head seemed to be thoroughly preoccupied with this task, but the left-hand one was grinning a broad, relaxed, nonchalant grin." (The Hitch Hiker's Guide to the Galaxy, Douglas Adams, 1979, published by Pan Macmillan).

In the BBC television adaptation (1981) Zaphod was played by Mark Wing-Davey and in the wide-screen version (2005) by Sam Rockwell.

---

2 July: Selman Abraham Waksman (1888-1973)
Discovery of streptomycin, Nobel prize 1952

CURIOUS FOLK CURES

Cure-all
Necklaces of amber (Pliny, *Natural History*, 77 AD)

Demonic possession
Dust from the pavement of the church on which the water that had washed the bones of King Oswald had been spilt (The Venerable Bede, *Historia Ecclesiastica*, 731)

Dog bites and excoriations
Fresh onions applied topically (Pliny, *Natural History*, 77 AD)

Fever
Green lizard alive in a vessel and worn as an amulet (Pliny, *Natural History*, AD 77)
Give as much of the clean web of a house spider as the weight of two scruples the night before the fit ... After the second dose, it will leave them (E Albin, *Natural History of Spiders*, 1736)

Nosebleeds
Cut an ash of one, two, or three years' growth at the very hour and minute of the Sun's entering into Taurus: a chip of this applied will stop nosebleed (John Aubrey, *Miscellanies*, 1696)

Scrofula (King's Evil)
Contact of the hand of a person who has been carried off by early death (Pliny, *Natural History*, 77 AD)

Smallpox
Take a scarlet or other red cloth, and put it about the pox; as I did to the King of England's son and the smallpox ceased in him, and I permitted only red things to be about his bed, by the which I cured him (John of Gaddesden, *Rosa Angelica*, 1314)

Sore eyes
Some commend May-dew gathered from Fennell and Celandine, to be most excellent for sore-eyes (Platt, *Delights for Ladies*, 1602)

Whooping-cough
Passing a child three times under the belly of an ass (Robert Southey, *Letters*, 1823)

> 4 July: Thomas John Barnardo (1845-1905)
> Medical philanthropist and founder of homes for street children

Tobacco

Tobacco is prepared from the leaves of the plant *Nicotiana tabacum*, which was first introduced into France by the Portuguese Joan Nicot, and into England by Sir Walter Raleigh in 1586. Apart from its use in cigars, cigarettes, and snuff, it has been used to treat:

Constipation
Hysteria
Lead poisoning
Strangulated hernia
Tetanus
Urethral stricture
Urinary retention
Worms

Fingers and teeth that are stained brown by cigarettes are stained with tar, not nicotine, as popular belief has it.

Pieces of poetry:
The lady with the lamp

The wounded from the battle-plain,
In dreary hospitals of pain,
   The cheerless corridors,
   The cold and stony floors.

Lo! In that house of misery
A lady with a lamp I see
   Pass through the glimmering gloom,
   And flit from room to room.

And slow, as in a dream of bliss,
The speechless sufferer turns to kiss
   Her shadow, as it falls
   Upon the darkening walls.

Extract from Henry Wadsworth Longfellow,
Santa Filomena (1857)

---

5 July: Herbert Spencer Gasser (1888-1963)
Discovery of functions of neurons, Nobel prize 1944

ETYMOLOGY: FOREIGN HICCUPS

The word hiccup in English is onomatopoieic, as it is in many other languages.
It should not be spelt hiccough, since it is nothing to doing with coughing.

Greek	lynx, a hiccup (also meant a convulsive sob)
Latin	singultus (also the technical medical term, infrequently used)
Italian	singhiozzo
Portuguese	soluco
German	schlucken
French	hoquet
Spanish	hipo
Russian	ikota
Old English	geocsian (to hiccup or sob)

ANCIENT CURES: HEADACHE

Binding the temples with the halter with which a man has been hanged
(Pliny, *Natural History*, 77 AD)

Pigeon's blood, applied to the soles of the feet
(Francis Bacon, *Sylva Sylvarum*, 1627)

Corner of a sheet that has wrapped a corpse
(Speranza Wilde, mother of Oscar Wilde, 1877)

Snakeskins placed within hats
(Jefferies, *Gamekeeper at Home*, 1877)

Driving a nail into a skull's head
(Folklore, 1977)

FAMOUS SUFFERERS:
PARKINSON'S DISEASE

*Muhammad Ali   Sir John Betjeman   Johnny Cash
Salvador Dali   Michael J Fox   Francisco Franco   Billy Graham
Katharine Hepburn   Arthur Koestler
William Masters   Pope John Paul II
Enoch Powell   Vincent Price
Michael Redgrave   Terry Thomas*

---

6 July: Axel Hugo Teodor Theorell (1903-1982)
Discovery of oxidative enzymes, Nobel prize 1955

PIECES OF POETRY: X-RAYS

The New Photography

O Röntgen, then the news is true,
    And not a trick of idle rumour,
That bids us each beware of you,
    And of your grim and graveyard humour.

We do not want, like Dr SWIFT,
    To take our flesh off and to pose in
Our bones, or show each little rift
    And joint for you to poke your nose in.

Punch, 1896

COLLEGE MOTTOES

CUM SCIENTIA CARITAS
Science with compassion
Royal College of General Practitioners

VITA DONUM DEI
Life is a gift from God
Royal College of Midwives

SUPER ARDUA
Let us overcome difficulties
Royal College of Obstetricians and Gynaecologists

QUAE PROSUNT OMNIBUS ARTES
Arts that benefit all mankind (Ovid, *Metamorphoses*)
Royal College of Surgeons

SEDES ET INVENIRE CAUSAS MORBORUM
To find out the seat and causes of disease
Royal College of Pathologists

LET WISDOM GUIDE (*Ecclesiastes*, Chapter 7)
Royal College of Psychiatrists

---

7 July: Camillo Golgi (1843-1926)
Structure of the nervous system, Nobel prize 1906

DEVIL'S DICTIONARY DEFINITIONS

The dates of the American journalist and author Ambrose Bierce are usually given as 1842-?1914. The question mark is added because in 1913 Bierce went South, seeking what he called "the good, kind darkness" in the Mexican Civil War, and was never seen again. Although he was best known in his lifetime as America's finest satiric journalist, Bierce is nowadays remembered for his ghostly short stories and *The Devil's Dictionary.*

Accident
An inevitable occurrence due to the action of immutable natural laws

Apothecary
The physician's accomplice, undertaker's benefactor and grave-worm's provider

Body-snatcher
One who supplies the young physicians with that which the old physicians have supplied the undertaker

Dentist
A prestidigitator who puts metal in your mouth, pulls coins out of your pocket

Diagnosis
A physician's forecast of disease by the patient's pulse and purse

Diaphragm
A muscular partition separating disorders of the chest from disorders of the bowels

Disease
Nature's endowment of medical schools

Doctor
A gentleman who thrives upon disease and dies of health

Epidermis
The thin integument which lies immediately outside the skin and immediately inside the dirt

Gout
A physician's name for the rheumatism of a rich patient

---

11 July: Thomas Bowdler (1754-1825)
Scottish physician and bowdlerizing publisher

DEVIL'S DICTIONARY DEFINITIONS (cont'd)

Grave
A place in which the dead are laid to await the coming of the medical student

Hearse
Death's baby-carriage

Homoeopathist
The humorist of the medical profession

Homoeopathy
A school of medicine midway between Allopathy and Christian Science. To the last both the others are distinctly inferior, for Christian Science will cure imaginary diseases, and they can not

Hospital
A place where the sick generally obtain two kinds of treatment - medical by the doctor and inhuman by the superintendent

Hyena
A beast held in reverence by some oriental nations from its habit of frequenting at night the burial-places of the dead. But the medical student does that

Indigestion
A disease which the patient and his friends frequently mistake for deep religious conviction and concern for the salvation of mankind

Oesophagus
That portion of the alimentary canal that lies between pleasure and business

Prescription
A physician's guess at what will best prolong the situation with least harm to the patient

Physician
One upon whom we set our hopes when ill and our dogs when well

Quack
A murderer without a license

---

16 July: Bela Schick (1877-1967)
Hungarian paediatrician, inventor of the Schick test for diphtheria

EUPHEMISMS: CONTRACEPTIVES

Armour
Bareback rider
Birth control
Bung
Cardigan
Circular protector
Collapsible container
Dutch cap
French letter
French tickler
Fight in armour
Get fitted
Joy bag
Johnny
On the loop
Malthusianism
On the pill
Precautions
Preventive
Pro-pack
Prophylactic
Protector
Raincoat
Rubber
Sheath
Skin
Something for the weekend
Tablet
Vatican roulette
Welly
Will there be anything else?

FAMOUS SUFFERERS: PROSTATE CANCER

Don Ameche   King Baudouin   Charles de Gaulle
James Herriott   Ayatollah Khomeini   Michael Korda   Timothy Leary
François Mitterand   Linus Pauling   Cornelius Ryan
Telly Savalas   Frank Zappa

19 July: Charles Horace Mayo (1865-1939)
Co-founder of the Mayo clinic

CLASSICS: THE EBERS PAPYRUS

This is one of the four most well preserved medical papyri in existence (the others being the Berlin, the Edwin Smith, and the Hearst). An Egyptian compilation of medical texts dated approximately 1550 BC, it was found between a mummy's legs in a tomb near Luxor, put up for sale, and acquired in 1873 by Professor George Maurice Ebers, an Egyptologist and novelist.

In addition to containing an exhaustive pharmacopoeia of around 700 formulations and folk remedies for conditions as wide-ranging as crocodile bites and toenail pain, along with remedies to rid the house of pests such as rats, flies, and scorpions, it also contains a very accurate description of the circulation of blood, with the heart at the centre of the cardiovascular system.

PIECES OF POETRY: ALCOHOL

Nothing in *Nature's Sober* found,
But an eternal *Health* goes round.
Fill up the *Bowl* then, fill it high,
Fill all the *Glasses* there, for why
Should every creature drink but *I*,
Why, *Man of Morals*, tell me why?

Extract from Anacreon, *Drinking*
Translated by Abraham Cowley (*Anacreontiques*, 1656)

A MEDICAL GAZETTEER

Doctor Arroyo   Doctor Belisario Dominguez   Doctor Coss   Doctor Mora
(all towns in Mexico)
Doctor Hicks Range, Australia
Doctor Pedro P Peña, Paraguay
Doctor Petru Groza, Romania (now called Sei)
Medicine Bow   Medicine Creek   Medicine Lake   Medicine Lodge
(all in the USA)
Nursling, Hampshire, England
Drug, Pakistan

20 July: Tadeus Reichstein (1897-1996)
Discovery of hormones of adrenal cortex, Nobel prize 1950

MYTHOLOGICAL MEDICINE

Achilles tendon
Insertion of the gastrocnemius muscle of the calf into the calcaneum
*Achilles was the son of the mortal Peleus and the sea-nymph Thetis. As an
infant, his mother held him by his heel and dipped him into the river Styx to
make him immortal, but this left his heel vulnerable. He was killed by a
poisoned arrow fired into his heel from the bow of Paris at the siege of Troy.*

Atlas
Alternative name for the first cervical vertebra
*Atlas was a Titan in Greek mythology who carried the vault of the sky on his
shoulders and was turned to stone by Perseus, son of Zeus, using Medusa's
head.*

Caput Medusae
Wavy dilated superficial umbilical veins secondary to portal hypertension
*Medusa was one of the three Gorgons in Greek mythology whose heads were
entwined with snakes. Those who encountered her gaze turned to stone.
Perseus used a mirrored shield to see her indirectly and decapitated her.*

Erysichthon syndrome
Coronary artery disease progression in overeating obese individuals; related to
Falstaff obesity
*In Greek mythology, Erysichthon, who despised the gods, cut down a sacred
oak and was condemned to insatiable hunger, eventually devouring himself.*

Hymen
Thin mucous membranous fold closing lower end of the vaginal introitus
*In Greek mythology, Hymenaeus was the son of Apollo and a
Muse, who was so beautiful that he was thought to be a girl.*

Iris
The circular membrane that separates the anterior and posterior
chambers of the eye
*Greek goddess of the rainbow, daughter of Thaumas and
Electra and sister of the Harpies.*

---

22 July: Gregor Johann Mendel (1822-1884)
Founding father of genetics

MYTHOLOGICAL MEDICINE (cont'd)

Priapism
Persistent painful erection of the penis, often unrelated to sexual activity
*The son of Dionysus and Aphrodite, Priapus was born with an enormous penis.
He is the protector of vineyards, gardens, and orchards.*

Proteus syndrome
A complex multisystem disorder with gigantism
*Proteus was a god of the sea, with the gift of prophecy, who was in charge of
tending to Poseidon's sea-creatures. John Merrick (The Elephant Man) suffered
from this genetic disorder, as possibly did Quasimodo.*

Ulysses syndrome
False-positive clinical investigations leading to mental and physical disorders
*Odysseus (Ulysses to the Romans) was the subject of Homer's epic poem The
Odyssey. The syndrome is named after Ulysses' long journey home after the
siege of Troy, with its many wayward adventures.*

SHAKESPEARE ON SYPHILIS

Consumption sow
In hollow bones of man; strike their sharp shins,
And mar men's spurring. Crack the lawyer's voice,
That he may never more false title plead,
Nor sound his quillets shrilly. Hoar the flamen,
That scolds against the quality of the flesh,
And not believes himself. Down with the nose,
Down with it flat, take the bridge quite away
Of him that, his particular to foresee,
Smells from the great weal. Make curl'd-pate ruffians bald,
And let the unscarr'd braggarts of the war
Derive some pain from you. Plague all,
That your activity may defeat and quell
The source of all erection.

Timon (Act IV, Scene 3)

28 July: Baruch Samuel Blumberg (1925-)
Identification of Australia antigen, Nobel prize 1976

SOME BRITISH ROYAL DEATHS

William I "the Conqueror" (died 1087) *Fell off his horse while riding through the town of Nantes as it burned, having entered into war with Philip I of France. He was buried in the abbey he had founded at Caen.*

William II "Rufus" (the Red) (died 1100) *Hunting in the New Forest, he was shot dead with an arrow supposedly fired by a Norman Knight named William Tyrrell.*

Henry I (died 1135) *"King Henry [I] being in Normandy, after some writers, fell from or with his horse, whereof he caught his death; but Ranulphe says he took a surfeit by eating of a lamprey, and thereof died".*

Richard I "Coeur de Lion" (died 1199) *He died when a shoulder wound from an arrow received during the siege of the castle of Chalus-Chabrol became infected, with resulting septicaemia.*

John (died 1216) *He died of dysentery in Newark while campaigning in the Fens.*

Edward II (died 1327) *Murdered in Berkeley castle in Gloucestershire, supposedly by having a red hot poker thrust up his Elephant and Castle.*

Henry IV (died 1413) *Died of a slow wasting disease (possibly diabetes), described by some as "leprosy".*

Henry V (died 1422) *Dysentery.*

Henry VI (died 1471) *Murdered in the Tower on the orders of Richard III.*

Mary II (died 1694) *Smallpox.*

William III (died 1704) *"He urged his horse to strike into a gallop just at a spot where a mole had been at work. Sorrel stumbled on the mole-hill, and went down on his knees. The King fell off and broke his collar-bone." Lord Macaulay, History of England, Chapter 25, 1849.*

George II (died 1760) *Massive heart attack at Kensington Palace.*

George VI (died 1952) *Died of a blood clot, at Sandringham, after a good day's shooting.*

> 29 July: Armauer Gerhard Henrik Hansen (1841-1912)
> Discovery of the leprosy bacillus

PIECES OF POETRY: CANCER

I wish I had the voice of Homer
To sing of rectal Carcinoma,
Which kills a lot more chaps, in fact,
Than were bumped off when Troy was sacked.
I noticed I was passing blood
(Only a few drops, not a flood).
So passing on my homeward way
From Tallahassee to Bombay
I asked a doctor, now my friend,
To peer into my hinder end,
To prove or disprove the rumor
That I had a malignant tumor.

By John Burdon Sanderson Haldane,
From *Cancer's A Funny Thing*, *New Statesman* (1964)

ANATOMICALLY ENTITLED: HANDS

A Handful of Dust
*Novel by Evelyn Waugh (1934); the title is a quote from The Waste Land by
TS Eliot, "I will show you fear in a handful of dust"*

The Moving Finger
*Detective story by Agatha Christie (1942); the title is a reference to the story of
Nebuchadnezzar in Daniel and a direct quote from The Rubáiyát of Omar
Khayyám in Edward Fitzgerald's translation (1859): "The moving finger writes
and, having writ, moves on"*

A Fistful of Dollars
*Spaghetti Western film (1964), directed by Sergio Leone, with memorable
music by Ennio Morricone, based on Akira Kurosawa's film "Yojimbo"; the first
to star Clint Eastwood as the "man with no name" (although in fact the credits
call him Joe); its two successful sequels were "For A Few Dollars More" (1965)
and "The Good, the Bad and the Ugly" (1966)*

The Hand that Rocks the Cradle
*Film about a murdering nanny, directed by Curtis Hanson (1991); the title is
from the saying "The hand that rocks the cradle rules the world"*

---

1 August: Jean Baptiste Lamarck (1744-1829)
Invention of the discredited doctrine of Lamarckism

FETUS OR FOETUS?

Fetus derives from the Latin word *feto*, I breed, but the spelling "foetus" has been around since at least the beginning of the seventh century. St Isidore, Archbishop of Seville, in a section entitled "De homine et partibus eius" in his *Originum sive etymologiarum libri (Books of Origins or Etymologies)*, commonly known as the *Etymologiae* (published in about 620 AD), incorrectly wrote that it was derived from *foveo*, I keep warm: "Foetus autem nominatus, quod adhuc in utero foveatur" (XI, 1, 144). "Fetus" is correct.

SUICIDE IN OPERA: CUTS AND STABS

L'Incoronazione di Poppea (Claudio Monteverdi, 1643)
Seneca the philosopher cuts open his veins in the bath at the command of the Emperor Nero relayed to him by Mercury

Ernani (Giuseppe Verdi, 1847)
The bandit Ernani (the former Don Juan of Aragon) stabs himself with a dagger in fulfilment of a pledge to die when his enemy Don Rui Gomez de Silva sounds his hunting horn

La Gioconda (Amilcare Ponchiella, 1876)
Gioconda the Venetian street singer stabs herself to frustrate the lust of the spy and her would-be lover and spy Barnaba

Madame Butterfly (Giacomo Puccini, 1904)
Cio-Cio-San stabs herself with her father's ceremonial sword to preserve her honour after Pinkerton's marriage to another woman

Turandot (Giacomo Puccini, 1926)
The slave-girl Liu stabs herself rather than betray under torture the name of the Unknown Prince, Calaf

Other suicidal operatic stabbings include:
Gwendoline (Gwendoline, Emmanuel Chabrier)
Herodiade (Salome, Jules Massenet)
Herman (The Queen of Spades, Tchaikovsky)

---

6 August: Alexander Fleming (1881-1955)
Discovery of penicillin, Nobel prize 1945

ATHLETIC ALLOPATHS

Sir Roger Bannister (1929-)
*English neurologist and athlete, born in Harrow and educated at Merton
College, Oxford, completing his medical training at St Mary's Hospital
in 1954. On 6 May 1954, he became the first man to run a mile in under
5 minutes at Iffley Road, Oxford. His exact time was 3 minutes 59.4 seconds.
He later retired from athletics to concentrate on his career in neurology, and
subsequently became Master of Pembroke College, Oxford.*

Roger Anthony Black MBE (1966-)
*Born in Portsmouth, England, he read medicine at Southampton
University but pursued a career in athletics. He went on to win fifteen major
championship medals, the highlight being a silver medal in the 1996 Olympic
400 metres final.*

Stephanie Cook MBE (1972-)
*Born in Irvine, Scotland, she was educated at Peterhouse College, Cambridge
and read medicine at Lincoln College, Oxford. She won the gold medal in the
modern pentathlon at the 2000 Sydney Olympics.*

Lord Arthur Espie Porritt (1900-1994)
*Born in Wanganui, New Zealand, he studied medicine at Selwyn College,
Otago and at Magdalen College, Oxford. He won the bronze medal in the
100-yard race at the 1924 Paris Olympics, the gold going to Harold
Abrahams. The race was immortalized in the film Chariots of Fire, but owing
to his modesty, a fictional "Tom Watson" portrayed the bronze medallist. He
was later appointed President of the Royal College of Surgeons of England,
President of the British Medical Association, and Governor-General of New
Zealand.*

FAMOUS SUFFERERS:
MULTIPLE SCLEROSIS

*Betty Cuthbert   Sir Augustus Frederic D'Este
Jacqueline du Pré   Dino Ferrari   Annette Funicello
William Hartnell   Heinrich Heine   David Lander
Alan Osmond   Richard Pryor   Montel Williams*

---

11 August: Christiaan Eijkman (1858-1930)
Discovery of thiamine, Nobel prize 1929

AGATHA CHRISTIE: DEATH BY POISON

Aconite
4.50 from Paddington (1957)

Adrenaline
One, Two, Buckle My Shoe (1940)

Arsenic
They Came to Baghdad (1951)

Atropine
The Thumb Mark of St Peter (1932)

Barbiturates
*Cards on the Table (1936); One, Two, Buckle My Shoe (1940);
Lord Edgware Dies (1933); The Murder of Roger Ackroyd (1926)*

Boomslang venom
Death in the Clouds (1935)

Cyanide
*The Big Four (1927); The Mirror Crack'd from Side to Side (1962); Sparkling
Cyanide (1945); A Pocketful of Rye (1953)*

Digitalis
*Appointment with Death (1938); Crooked House (1949);
Postern of Fate (1973)*

Glyceryl trinitrate
The Chocolate Box (1925)

Oxalic acid
Murder is Easy (1939)

Physostigmine
Crooked House (1949); Curtain (1975)

Ricin
The House of Lurking Death (1929)

---

13 August: Salvador Edward Luria (1912-1991)
Viral replication mechanism & genetic structure, Nobel prize 1969

AGATHA CHRISTIE: DEATH BY POISON (cont'd)

Strychnine
The Mysterious Affair at Styles (1920)

Taxine
A Pocket Full of Rye (1953)

Thallium
The Pale Horse (1961)

THE EYE OF HORUS

The R_x symbol is well known as the sign of a prescription, and it is often said that it is Rx, a shortened version of the Latin word recipe. But R_x is not R plus x; it is a corruption of a symbol that was once used by the ancient Egyptians to signify the *utchat*, the eye of Horus.

Horus the Elder had two eyes, the sun and the moon. Set, the god of night and darkness, evil and death, stole the sun, but Thoth made a treaty between them and allotted the day to Horus and the night to Set. Set was not content, however, and continued to make war on Horus by regularly cutting off parts of the moon, while Thoth renewed it each month (an interesting explanation of a natural phenomenon).

Thus, the eye of Horus became a potent symbol of good fortune and healing, later adopted by the Greeks, Arabs, and others.

In recent years the belief that the sign R_x is formed from R (= recipe) plus x (somehow indicating an abbreviation) has led to the proliferation of numerous similar abbreviations, used as shorthand in medical case notes:

H_x for history
S_x for symptoms
I_x for investigations
D_x for diagnosis
M_x for management
Ab_x for antibiotics

---

15 August: Gerty Theresa Radnitz Cori (1896-1957)
Discovery of the catalytic conversion of glycogen, Nobel prize 1947

SARDONIC SLANG

10th floor transfer	*Dying*
45C	*Patient one short of a full set of chromosomes*
Acute hyponicotaemia	*Desperate for a fag*
Ash cash	*Money for signing a cremation form*
Angel lust	*A male corpse with an erection*
Assmosis	*Career promotion brown-nosing*
Bagged and tagged	*Dead body ready for transfer to the morgue*
Bash cash	*Cash for completing accident-related insurance forms*
Blamestorming	*Finding someone to blame (usually a locum or the most junior doctor)*
Bobbing for apples	*Manual evacuation*
Bungee jumper	*Patient who pulls on his catheter*
Bunny boiler	*Dangerously obsessive woman[1]*
Cabbage	*Coronary artery bypass graft*
Chocolate hostage	*Constipated*
Chrome-induced ischaemia	*Chest pains that suddenly develop in handcuffed patients*
Craniofaecal syndrome	*Not the brightest*
Craptopil	*Captopril*
Dagenham	*Severe madness (three stops beyond Barking)*
Departure lounge	*Geriatric ward*
Eating in	*Intravenous feeding*
Eternal care	*Intensive care (for those who will never return...)*
Expensive care	*Intensive care*
Feet-up general	*Quiet district general hospital*
Fluttering eye syndrome	*Patient faking unconsciousness*
Genital hurties	*Genital herpes*
Guessing tubes	*Stethoscope*
House red	*Blood*
Inbreds	*Doctors whose parents are doctors*
Insurance whiplash	*Neck pain secondary to a minor road traffic accident*
Lignocephalic	*Not the brightest*
Microdeckia	*Patient playing with less than a full deck*
Ooh, aahs	*People who gather at emergencies to gawk*
Pneumocephalic	*Not the brightest*
Retrospectoscope	*Instrument of hindsight*
Rocking horse manure	*Even rarer than hen's teeth*
Smurf sign	*Patient blue or going blue*

---

23 August: Hamilton Othanel Smith (1931-)
Discovery of restriction enzymes, Nobel prize 1978

SARDONIC SLANG (cont'd)

Throckmorton's sign (or PPP sign)	*Penis (or Percy) Points to Pathology*
Toaster	*Defibrillator*
Two stops short of West Ham	*Barking mad*
Unclear medicine	*Nuclear medicine*
Velcro	*Friends or relatives accompanying patients everywhere*
Viaggravation	*Patient demanding Viagra free on the NHS*
Woolworths test	*A patient fit enough to shop at Woolworths must be fit enough for general anaesthesia*

[1]From the behaviour of the character played by Glenn Close in the film *Fatal Attraction* (1987)

VARIETIES OF DROPSY

Dropsy of the legs (nowadays called peripheral oedema)
Cochlear hydrops (Menière's disease)
Corneal hydrops
Endolymphatic hydrops (Menière's disease)
Gallbladder dropsy
Hydrops (joint effusion)
Hydrops abdominis (ascites)
Hydrops amnii (hydramnios)
Hydrops fetalis (seen in rhesus disease)
Hydrops labyrinthi (Menière's disease)
Hydrops pectoris (pleural effusion)
Hydrops pericardii (pericardial effusion)
Hydrops tubae profluens (intermittent hydrosalpinx)
Meningeal hydrops (hydrocephalus)
Ovarium dropsy (ovarian cyst)

Epidemic dropsy, which is seen mostly in India, but has also been reported in Mauritius, Fiji, South Africa, and Nepal, is due to the ingestion of mustard oil or ghee adulterated with oil from the seeds of *Argemone mexicana* (the Mexican poppy), which contain a toxin called sanguinarine, first identified in *Sanguinaria canadensis*, the blood-root. Epidemic dropsy causes gastrointestinal symptoms followed by pitting oedema of the legs, fever, and darkening of the skin, often with local erythema and tenderness. Perianal itching is common, and myocarditis and heart failure can occur.

---

24 August: Albert Claude (1898-1983)
Internal composition of cells, Nobel prize 1974

FAMOUS SIAMESE TWINS

The Biddenden Maids, England, 1100-34
The Hungarian Sisters, 1701-23
Chang and Eng, the original Siamese twins, 1811-74
Rita-Christina, Sardinia, 1829-?
Millie-Christine, USA, 1951-?
Rosa and Josepha Blazek, Bohemia, 1878-1922
The Chen Brothers, China, 1886-?
Radica-Doodica, India, 1900 (separated 1902)
Simplicio and Lucio Godina, Philippines, 1908-36
The Honduras Twins, 1906-?
Daisy and Violet Hilton, England, 1908-? (featured in Tod Hunter's film
Freaks, 1936)
The Gibbs Sisters, USA, dates unknown
Guarabai and Guaganbai, India, exhibited in Paris 1931

ANATOMICALLY ENTITLED: BREASTS

The Breast-Plate of Faith and Love

By John Preston (1630). "A treatise wherein the ground and exercise of faith and love, as they are set upon Christ their object, and as they are expressed in good words, is explained. Delivered in 18 sermons upon three severall texts."

The Breast

Novella by Philip Roth (1972), about a man, David Alan Kepesh, who thinks he has been turned into a breast. Roth's other tales about Kepesh are "The Professor of Desire" (1977) and "The Dying Animal" (2001).

Les Mamelles de Tiresias

Opera by Francis Poulenc (1947) based on the Greek legend of the blind prophet Tiresias, who had been both a man and a woman during his long life. When Zeus and Hera quarrelled about which of the two sexes gained more pleasure from sexual congress, they agreed to ask Tiresias. He said that the woman did. In anger, Hera smote him blind; to compensate, Zeus gave him the dubious gift of prophecy. In a less interesting version, Athene, whom he saw bathing, struck him blind and then, contrite, conferred the gift of prophesy.

---

25 August: Hans Adolf Krebs (1900-1981)
Discovery of the citric acid cycle, Nobel prize 1953

SUICIDE IN OPERA: POISONS

Il Trovatore (Giuseppe Verdi, 1853)
*Leonora, lady-in-waiting to the Princess of Aragon, takes poison from a ring
and swallows it to avoid the clutches of the Count di Luna*

L'Africaine (Jacques Meyerbeer, 1865)
*Selika inhales the perfume of the manchineel tree, a poisonous West Indian tree
(Hippomani mancinella or Euphorbia cotinifolia), which contains phorbol
esters, highly toxic compounds causing symptoms such as skin blistering*

L'Amore Dei Trei Re (Italo Montemezzi, 1910)
Manfredo kisses the poisoned lips of his murdered wife as she lies in her tomb

Suor Angelica (Giacomo Puccini, 1918)
*Sister Angelica concocts a poisonous potion
from herbs in her garden and kills herself*

The Consul (Gian Carlo Menotti, 1950)
Magada Sorel seals herself in her kitchen and turns on the gas

SHAKESPEARE ON DROWNING

O Lord, methought what pain it was to drown,
What dreadful noise of water in my ears,
What sights of ugly death within my eyes!
Methought I saw a thousand fearful wrecks,
A thousand men that fishes gnaw'd upon,
Wedges of gold, great anchors, heaps of pearl,
Inestimable stones, unvalued jewels,
All scatt'red in the bottom of the sea;
Some lay in dead men's skulls, and in those holes
Where eyes did once inhabit they were crept,
As 'twere in scorn of eyes, reflecting gems,
That woo'd the slimy bottom of the deep
And mock'd the dead bones that lay scatt'red by.

King Richard III (Act III, Scene 4)

---

26 August: Charles Robert Richet (1850-1935)
Immunologist, Nobel prize for work on anaphylaxis 1913

PIONEERING PRACTITIONERS

Alcmaeon of Crotona (fl. c535 BC)
Credited as the originator of experimental psychology, he pioneered studies in natural philosophy, pathoanatomy, and physical aspects of internal disease.

Antyllus (fl. c110-130 AD)
Quoted by Galen, this surgeon studied venesection and cupping, and published detailed instructions for operations (e.g. cataracts and tracheotomy).

Averroes (d. 1198 AD)
This Spanish-born physician, whose full name was Abu-l-Walid Muhammad ibn Ahmad ibn Muhammad ibn Rushd, is best known for his commentaries on Aristotle. He wrote a major medical encyclopaedia, called al-Kulliyat ("The Book of General Principles"), which deals with anatomy, health, pathology, symptoms, dietetics and drugs, hygiene, and therapeutics.

Erastratus (c300-250 BC)
He abandoned the doctrine of humours for explaining the origin of disease, and expounded a complete physiological scheme of the body. He proposed that the heart was at the centre of the circulation and the source of arteries and veins. He was thus ahead of medical opinion in this area until William Harvey in 1628. He is also credited with inventing the first catheter and the first calorimeter.

Huang Ti (c2700-2600 BC)
Author of a classic medical treatise, Nei Ching Su Wen, the oldest known written medical work. He taught five basic therapeutic forms: acupuncture, diet, pharmacological remedies, spiritual cures, and treatment of the respiratory and excretory systems. The Nei Ching is the foundation of modern acupuncture.

Imhotep (c2667- 2648 BC)
Widely regarded in ancient Egypt as a knowledgeable physician, he was credited with saving the life of the wife of Pharaoh Khasekhem during childbirth. He is also believed to be the author of the Edwin Smith Papyrus. He is best known, however, as the chief architect of the step pyramid at Saqqara.

Mar Samuel (or Shmuel ben Abba Hakohen) (c180-c254 AD)
The most renowned physician in the Talmud, his medical pronouncements included anatomy, blood-letting,, dermatology, embryology, obstetrics, ophthalmology, paediatrics, therapeutics, toxicology, urology, and wound healing.

---

28 August: Sir Godfrey Newbold Hounsfield (1919-2004)
Development of CT scanning, Nobel prize 1979

PIONEERING PRACTITIONERS (cont'd)

Soranus of Ephesus (98-138 AD)
Considered the father of obstetrics, his works also dealt with diagnostics, fracture surgery, the history of medicine, hygiene, nervous disorders, and problems of terminology. His Gynaecology tells of Roman beliefs regarding the female reproductive system, abortion, birth control, fertility, midwifery, and family planning. His opinions on women's and infants' care persisted until the end of the Renaissance.

Zhang Zhongjing or Zhang Ji (fl. 210 AD)
A famous physician near the end of the Han dynasty, he wrote several medical works, including Shang Han Za Bin Lun (Treatise on Being Affected by Cold). This had information about diseases caused by the pathogenic factor "han" (cold). He showed how this can be diagnosed (especially by pulse diagnosis) and what its origins were.

EUPHEMISMS: FEMALE GENITALIA

Beard
Beaver
Between the legs
Bird
Box
Bush
Cupid's cave
Down below
Fanny
Gap
Garden of Eden
Hole
It
Nest
Muff
Private parts
Pussy
Secret parts
Slit
Snatch
Touch-hole
Velvet

29 August: Werner Theodor Otto Forssmann (1904-1979)
Invention of cardiac catheterization, Nobel prize 1956

DISEASES NAMED AFTER OCCUPATIONS OR PURSUITS

Athlete's foot
Bird fancier's lung
Breast-stroker's knee
Chauffeur's fracture
Chimneysweeper's scrotum
Clergyman's knee
Coal miner's nystagmus
Farmer's lung
Footballer's ankle
Gamekeeper's thumb
Golfer's elbow
Hatter's shakes
Housemaid's knee
Jogger's nipple
Jumper's knee
Knitter's finger
Little leaguer's elbow
Malt worker's lung

Mariner's tuberculosis
Matchmaker's phossy jaw
Mushroom picker's lung
Painter's colic
Pigeon fancier's lung
Pitcher's shoulder
Potter's rot
Pugilist's encephalopathy
Skater's heel (pump-bump)
Skier's thumb
Slot-machine sprain
Space Invader's wrist
Spinner's thumb (cricket)
Student's elbow
Swimmer's shoulder
Telegrapher's cramp
Water skier's rectum
Weaver's bottom

ANATOMICAL IDIOMS

Keep your hair on
See eye to eye
The sweat of one's brow
Down in the mouth
A sweet tooth
A lump in the throat
Breakneck speed
Elbow grease
Smite hip and thigh
A leg to stand on
Knee-jerk reaction
Start on the wrong foot
Dig one's heels in
A toehold

Heads will roll
Not bat an eyelid
Nose dive
Bite one's lip
Fed up to the back teeth
Turn the other cheek
Shoulder the blame
The back of beyond
Spineless
Close to one's chest
Make a clean breast
Bosom friends
Have a bellyful
Lap of luxury

Face saving
Raise your eyebrows
Ears burning
Jaws of death
A sharp tongue
Lead with one's chin
Twist one's arm
Slap on the wrist
Hand over fist
Grease one's palm
Light fingered
Under one's thumb
Cut to the quick
Knuckle under

31 August: Maria Montessori (1870-1952)
The first Italian woman to qualify as a doctor

Bedside library for medical students (our recommendations)

Fiction

- *Dr Glas* by Hjalmar Söderberg (1905). A doctor, corrupted by his love for a beautiful woman, murders her husband. Reworked by Dannie Abse in *The Strange Case of Dr Simmonds & Dr Glas* (2002).
- *The Horseman on the Roof* by Jean Giono (1951). Love in the time of cholera in 19th century France. Also an excellent movie (1995).
- *Doctor in the House* by Richard Gordon (1952). Although over 50 years old, this elegant evocation of a London teaching hospital in the fledgling National Health Service is still entertaining.
- *The Patient* by Georges Simenon (1963). How a stroke revolutionizes the life of a self-centred French journalist.
- *Master and Commander* by Patrick O'Brian (1970) and other books in the Aubrey/Maturin series. Life and doctoring at sea in the Napoleonic Wars.
- *The Bell Jar* by Sylvia Plath (1971). A novelistic evocation of depression; also Ted Hughes' poetic account of his relationship with Sylvia, *Birthday Letters* (1998).
- *Love in the Time of Cholera* by Gabriel García Márquez (1985). An epic anatomy of love by the Nobel prize-winning novelist.
- *The Cunning Man* by Robertson Davies (1994). Canadian physic.
- *Enduring Love* by Ian McEwan (1997). A novel abut De Clérambault's syndrome; the title has a double meaning - not just lasting love, but putting up with it. The film (2004) is an excellent rendition.
- *The Blood Doctor* by Barbara Vine (2002). A psychological mystery story about haemophilia.

Famous sufferers: Motor neuron disease

Dennis Day   Stephen Hawking
Charlie Mingus   David Niven   Dimitry Shostakovich
Mao Tse Tung   Michael Zaslow

---

3 September: Frank MacFarlane Burnet (1899-1985)
Discovery of acquired immunological tolerance, Nobel prize 1960

Anatomically entitled: Eyes

Eyeless in Gaza
*Novel by Aldous Huxley (1936), from Milton's poem Samson Agonistes (1671),
"Eyeless in Gaza, at the mill with slaves"*

Ommateum
*Poems by A R Ammons (1955), the ommateum being the word for an insect's
compound eye*

An Eye for an Eye
*Film directed by Christian Matras (1956), in which a doctor has to make a
long journey with a demented man whose wife has died under his care.*

The Man With X-ray Eyes
Film directed by Roger Corman, starring Ray Milland (1963)

The Eye
*Novella by Vladimir Nabokov (1965). The title is a homophone of the Russian
title, which is pronounced, according to Nabokov himself, "Sugly-dart-eye",
which means a spy or watcher; so there is a connection*

Eyes
*Novel by Janet Burroway (1966), deals with medical ethics, as seen through
the eyes of an eye surgeon and his family*

Eyes Wide Shut
*The last film directed by Stanley Kubrick, starring the then husband-and-wife
couple of Tom Cruise and Nicole Kidman, as a married couple (1999)*

Doctors who did not practise

*Jean Frederic Bazille
Hector Berlioz
Che Guevara
William Harrison
David Livingstone
Gertrude Stein
W Somerset Maugham*

---

6 September: John James Rickard Macleod (1876-1935)
Discovery of insulin, Nobel prize 1923

PREFIX/SUFFIX

Prefix or suffix	Meaning	Origin	Example
a-	lacking	Greek	Achlorhydria, lacking hydrochloric acid in the stomach
ab-	away from	Latin	Abduction, movement away from
ad-	towards	Latin	Adduction, movement towards
an-	lacking	Latin	Anaemic, lacking blood
-aemia	blood	Greek	Thalassaemia, literally sea in the blood
aero-	air	Greek	Anaerobic bacteria, which can survive without air
arterio-	to do with arteries	Latin	Arteriopath, someone with severe arterial disease
cephal(o)-	the head	Greek	Cephalalgia, pain in the head
dys-	hard, painful, or faulty	Greek	Dyspnoea, difficulty in breathing Dyspareunia, pain during intercourse
di(a)-	through	Greek	Diarrhoea (through flow)
epi-	on or over	Greek	Epidermis, over the dermis, i.e. outer layer of the skin
e-, ex-	out of	Latin	Efferent, leading out of (the nervous system)
erythro-	red	Greek	Erythrocyte, a red blood cell
-gen(ic)	origin of	Greek	Carcinogen, a cancer-causing substance
glom-	tuft, ball, knot	Latin	Glomus, a tumour of blood vessels
gust-	taste	Latin	Gustation, appreciation of taste
-graph;	a writer	Greek	Electrocardiograph, a trace of heart rate and rhythm
hydro-	water	Greek	Hydrophobia, rabies, literally fear of water
leuko-	white	Greek	Leukocyte, a white blood cell
moto-	movement	Latin	Motoneuron, a neuron controlling muscle movement
necro-	death	Greek	Necrotic, dead (tissue)
neo-	new	Greek	Neoplasm, a new growth (i.e. cancer)
-penia	lack	Greek	Leukopenia, lack of white blood cells
pseudo-	false	Greek	Pseudogout, a condition that mimics gout
-rrhoea	[excess] flow	Greek	Diarrhoea, logorrhoea
semin-	seed	Latin	Seminal fluid, semen
vener-	sexual	Latin	Venereal, sexually transmitted

10 September: Thomas Sydenham (1624-89)
"The English Hipppocrates" and the father of English medicine

SOME MEDICAL MUSEUMS

Dittrick Medical History Center, Cleveland
Specializes in microscopes and surgical instruments

National Museum of Health and Medicine, Washington, DC (part of the Smithsonian Institution)
Includes the bullet that killed Abe Lincoln

Florence Nightingale Museum, Lambeth, London
The "Nightingale relics" include her coin collection and medicine chest

Freud Museum, Hampstead, London
Contains Freud's collection of antiquities from Egypt, Greece, Rome, and China

The Public Health Museum, Cambridge, Massachusetts
Includes a colourful collection of patent medicine bottles

Hunterian Museum, The Royal College of Surgeons of England, Holborn, London
Contains the collections of the previous Hunterian and Odontological Museums, including the skeletons of the Irish giant Charles Byrne and the Sicilian dwarf, Caroline Crachami, who at about 20 inches was once described as "the smallest of all persons mentioned in the records of littleness"

The Hunterian Museum, Glasgow
Contains many pathological specimens

Museum of the Royal College of Surgeons of Edinburgh, Edinburgh
Contains a large collection of surgical pathological specimens

Mütter Museum, College of Physicians of Philadelphia, Philadelphia
Contains a large collection of anatomical and pathological specimens, medical instruments, and memorabilia of individual doctors; includes examples of conjoined twins

The Old Operating Theatre, Museum and Herb Garret, St. Thomas' Hospital, Southwark, London
Includes a wide range of apothecary's instruments and jars

---

14 September: Margaret Sanger (1883-1966)
Pioneer of birth control

Hermaphrodites

A hermaphrodite is a person born with both male and female sex organs.

A true hermaphrodite has both ovaries and testicles, either separately or combined in a single organ. The genitalia are variable.

A female pseudohermaphrodite has normal female chromosomes but masculinized genitalia. Usually caused by congenital adrenal hyperplasia with overproduction of testosterone.

A male pseudohermaphrodite has normal male chromosomes and testes but female or ambiguous external genitalia. Usually caused by insensitivity to androgens.

Trees and Flowers in Medicine

Acne rosacea
Acneiform disorder of the skin and eye of unknown aetiology

Bamboo spine
Radiographic description of fusion of the spine in ankylosing spondylitis

Lichen planus
A violaceous skin eruption; lichen is from the Latin for "what eats around itself"

Mossy foot
Chronic lymphoedema

Pineal gland
Because it is like a tiny pinecone

Sunflower cataracts
Seen in Wilson's disease (a genetic disorder of copper metabolism)

---

16 September: Albert Szent-Györgyi (1893-1986)
Biochemist, Nobel prize for his discoveries in connection with the
biological combustion processes, with special reference to vitamin C
and the catalysis of fumaric acid 1937

Anatomically entitled: Heart

The Heart of Midlothian
Novel by Sir Walter Scott (1818); the title refers to the prison of that name in Edinburgh, in the county of Lothian in Scotland

Heartbreak House
Play by George Bernard Shaw (1919)

The Heart is a Lonely Hunter
Novel by Carson McCullers (1940); the title is from the poem The Lonely Hunter by Fiona MacLeod, a pseudonym of William Sharp: "My heart is a lonely hunter that hunts on a lonely hill"

The Heart of the Matter
Novel by Grahame Greene (1948), which deals with sin

Kind Hearts and Coronets
Film by Robert Hamer (1949) from the novel Israel Rank (1907) by Roy Horniman. In the film Alec Guinness played eight different members of the aristocratic D'Ascoyne family and Dennis Price their murderer. The title is from the poem Lady Clara Vere de Vere by Alfred Lord Tennyson (1842):
"Kind hearts are more than coronets
And simple faith more than Norman blood."

The Matter of the Heart
Novel by Nicholas Royle (1997) concerning events linked to a mad 19th-century doctor performing heart-swapping operations

Rectal foreign bodies

In 1986, Drs David B Busch and James R Starling from Madison, Wisconsin, USA published a scientific article entitled "Rectal foreign bodies: case report and a comprehensive review of the world's literature" (*Surgery* 1986; 100: 512-19). In it, they reviewed the large volume of prior literature on this subject and tabulated all previous cases by type and number of objects recovered, with a discussion of the patients' age distribution, history, complications, and prognosis (although not the patients' explanations of how they got there).

22 September: Charles Brenton Huggins (1901-1997)
Hormonal treatment of prostate cancer, Nobel prize 1966

Rectal foreign bodies (cont'd)

The following is a summary of objects recovered from the rectum:

Object	No.
Glass or ceramics (e.g. jars, bottles with attached rope, light bulb, tube)	58
Food (e.g. apple, banana, cucumber, plantain, salami, turnip)	19
Wooden objects (e.g. axe handle, broom handle)	14
Sexual devices (e.g. vibrator, dildo)	28
Kitchen device (e.g. knife, ice pick, knife sharpener, pestle and mortar)	8
Tools (e.g. flashlight, toothbrush, screwdriver, pen, wire spring, candle)	12
Inflated devices (e.g. balloon, balloon attached to a cylinder, condom)	3
Balls (e.g. baseball, tennis ball, pool cue ball)	4
Containers (e.g. baby powder can, candle box, shampoo bottle, snuff box)	4
Miscellaneous (e.g. bottle cap, gold chain, frozen pig's tail)	15

In addition, several "collections" in single patients were also presented:

Oilcan with potato stopper
Piece of wood and peanut
Umbrella handle and enema tubing
Phosphorus match ends (homicide)
402 stones
Toolbox (inside a convict - contained saws and other items usable in escape attempts)
Beer glass and preserving pot
Lemon and cold cream jar
Spectacles, suitcase key, tobacco pouch, and magazine

The classic text ***Bailey and Love's Short Practice of Surgery*** states:
The variety of foreign bodies that have found their way into the rectum, is hardly less remarkable than the ingenuity displayed in their removal. A turnip has been delivered per anum by the use of obstetric forceps. A stick firmly impacted has been withdrawn by inserting a gimlet into its lower end. A tumbler, mouth looking downwards, has been extracted by filling the interior with a wet plaster of Paris bandage, leaving the end of the bandage protruding, and allowing the plaster to set. If insurmountable difficulty is experienced in grasping any foreign body in the rectum, a left lower laparotomy is necessary, which allows that object to be pushed from above into the assistant's fingers in the rectum. If there is considerable laceration of the mucosa a temporary colostomy is advisable.

---

24 September: Howard Walter Florey (1898-1968)
Isolation of penicillin, Nobel prize 1945

PIECES OF PROSE:
PICKWICK AND HIS SYNDROME

A most violent and startling knocking was heard at the door; it was not an ordinary double knock, but a constant and uninterrupted succession of the loudest single raps, as if the knocker were endowed with the perpetual motion, or the person outside had forgotten to leave off...

The object that presented itself to the eyes of the astonished clerk, was a boy - a wonderfully fat boy - habited as a serving lad, standing upright on the mat, with his eyes closed as if in sleep. He had never seen such a fat boy, in or out of a travelling caravan; and this, coupled with the calmness and repose of his appearance, so very different from what was reasonably to have been expected in the inflicter of such knock, smote him with wonder.

"What's the matter?" inquired the clerk.

The extraordinary boy replied not a word; but he nodded once, and seemed, to the clerk's imagination, to snore feebly.

"Where do you come from?" inquired the clerk.

The boy made no sign. He breathed heavily, but in all other respects was motionless.

The clerk repeated the question thrice, and receiving no answer, prepared to shut the door, when the boy suddenly opened his eyes, winked several times, sneezed once, and raised his hand as if to repeat the knocking. Finding the door open, he stared about him with astonishment, and at length fixed his eyes on Mr. Lowten's face.

"What the devil do you knock in that way for?" inquired the clerk, angrily.

"Which way?" said the boy, in a slow and sleepy voice.

"Why, like forty hackney-coachmen," replied the clerk.

"Because master said, I wasn't to leave off knocking till they opened the door, for fear I should go to sleep," said the boy.

Extract from Charles Dickens,
The Pickwick Papers (1837)

Pickwickian syndrome, named after the fat, red-faced boy Joe, is obstructive sleep apnoea in obese patients, with increased blood concentrations of carbon dioxide and polycythaemia (increased number of red blood cells), leading to a plethoric face (meaning having an excessive amount of blood).

In 1839 George William MacArthur Reynolds, the English author and politician, founder of *Reynold's Miscellany* (1846), published a novel called *Pickwick Abroad*.

---

25 September: Thomas Hunt Morgan (1866-1945)
Discovery of chromosome function, Nobel prize 1933

SUICIDE IN OPERA: FUNERAL PYRE

Dido and Aeneas (Henry Purcell, 1689)
Dido stabs herself and then mounts her funeral pyre

Norma (Bellini, 1831)
*The Roman proconsul Pollione mounts the funeral pyre and joins the Druid
priestess Norma*

Götterdämmerung (Richard Wagner, 1876)
*Brunnhilde plunges her horse Grane on to Siegfried's funeral pyre,
which she has built*

Khovanshchina (Modest Mussorgsky, 1886)
*Members of the Old Believers, including Marfa and Andrea, commit
suicide on a funeral pyre in order to avoid religious reforms*

FAMOUS SUFFERERS: TUBERCULOSIS

*Alexander Graham Bell   Sarah Bernhardt   Simon Bolivar
Charlotte Bronte   Emily Bronte   Elizabeth Barrett Browning
Anton Chekhov   Frederic Chopin   Paul Ehrlich
Ralph Waldo Emerson   Edvard Grieg   Doc Holliday
Franz Kafka   John Keats   D. H. Lawrence
Vivien Leigh   Katherine Mansfield   W. Somerset Maugham
Amedeo Modigliani   Jean Molière   Napoleon II
Eugene O'Neill   George Orwell   Niccolo Paganini
Alexander Pope   Eleanor Roosevelt   Jean-Jacques Rousseau
Johann Schiller   Percy Bysshe Shelley   Baruch Spinoza
Robert Louis Stevenson   Igor Stravinsky   Henry David Thoreau
And the inventor of the stethoscope: René Theophile Hyacinthe Laennec*

And some fictional sufferers:
Louis Dubedat (*The Doctor's Dilemma* by George Bernard Shaw)
Hindley Earnshaw (*Wuthering Heights* by Emily Bronte)
Mimi (*Scènes de la Vie de Boheme* by Henri Murger)
Marguerite Gautier (*La Dame aux Camellias* by Alexandre Dumas fils; Violetta
in Puccini's operatic version, *La Traviata*)

---

27 September: Ivan Petrovich Pavlov (1849-1936)
Physiology of digestion, Nobel prize, 1904

ANATOMICALLY ENTITLED: PUDENDA

The Delta of Venus
Erotica by Anaïs Nin (1977); the several pieces in this collection were written to earn money while she was in Paris in the 1920s; the delta is the triangular pattern of pudendal hair over the mons veneris

Venusberg
Novel by Anthony Powell (1932); the title may refer to the mons veneris

A Maidenhead Well Lost
Play by Thomas Heywood (1634)

The Vagina Monologues
One-woman show by Eve Ensler (1998) subsequently performed by a trio

The Rubyfruit Jungle
Novel by Rita Mae Brown (1973) about the coming out of a lesbian; the title is the author's description of the female pudenda

Tunc
Novel (1968) by Lawrence Durrell. The possible anagrammatic reference to the female pudenda in the title was emphasized by the typography that was used on the original dust jacket, in which the U, N, and C all had the same shape, but in different orientations. Tunc and its sequel Numquam (1970) were collectively given the title The Revolt of Aphrodite (1974), reinforcing the sexual connection. Aut tunc aut numquam is Latin for now or never.

SHAKESPEARE ON GOUT

Yet am I better
Than one that's sick o' th' gout, since he had rather
Groan so in perpetuity than be cur'd
By th' sure physician death, who is the key
T' unbar these locks.

As spoken by Posthumus,
Cymbeline (Act V, Scene 4)

---

2 October: Christian de Duve (1917-1983)
Internal composition of cells, Nobel prize 1974

BIRDS IN MEDICINE

Chicken pox

Crow's feet

Dodo (dod) gene
One of four transcription units within the gene of Drosophila melanogaster; the others are called tweety (twe), flightless (fli), and penguin (pen)

Goose bumps

KIWI
The Kinmen Women-health Investigation, a menopausal study of a Taiwanese population aged 40-54

Parrot beak syndrome
Genetic disorder causing increased breadth at root of nose and whitened forelock

Pica
Pica is the Latin word for a magpie; pica is an eating disorder typically defined as the persistent eating of non-nutritive substances for a period of at least 1 month at an age in which this behaviour is developmentally inappropriate (e.g. >18-24 months)

Pigeon breast
Pectus carinatum

Pigeon toes
In-toeing

Seagull murmur
Heard in aortic regurgitation

Stork bite
Birthmark on neck

Swan neck deformity
Seen in the fingers in rheumatoid arthritis

Swan's neck osteotome
A surgical instrument

Cold turkey

---

8 October: Rodney Robert Porter (1917-1985)
Chemical structure of antibodies, Nobel prize 1972

CLASSICS: THE EDWIN SMITH PAPYRUS

This papyrus was discovered by the American Edwin Smith, a pioneer in the field of Egyptian science, in 1862 in Luxor at Thebes, and was bequeathed by him upon his death in 1906 to the New York Hospital Society. It was later passed on to American Egyptologist James Henry Breasted for study in 1920. It is an ancient Egyptian medical treatise and is believed to date from around 3000 BC.

It covers conditions from head to toe, beginning with clinical cases of head injuries and progressing down the body, detailing clinical examination, diagnosis, treatment, and prognosis in around 48 clinical cases. Details of the cardiovascular and gastrointestinal systems are also given.

SHAKESPEARE ON RABIES

...take heed of yonder dog!
Look when he fawns, he bites; and when he bites,
His venom tooth will rankle to the death:
Have not to do with him, beware of him;
Sin, death, and hell, have set their marks upon him...

King Richard III (Act I, Scene 3)

ANATOMICALLY ENTITLED: EARS

The Ear
A Czech film ("Ucho", 1970), a dark domestic and political drama, directed by Karel Kachyna; it was suppressed by the Soviet authorities for 20 years

Hearing Secret Harmonies
A novel by Anthony Powell (1975), the last in the sequence entitled "A Dance to the Music of Time". The title is a quote from the seventeenth century alchemist Thomas Vaughan, who spoke of death as the sphere "to which the liberated soul ascends, looking at the sunset towards the west wind and hearing secret harmonies"

---

13 October: Rudolph Virchow (1821-1902)
German pathologist who demonstrated that diseases were due to abnormalities of cells (the cell theory)

SAINTS IN MEDICINE

Saint	Connection
St Acacius	Headaches
St Agatha	Diseases of the breast
St Aignon	Tinea favosa (a type of tinea capitis)
St Aman	Pellagra
St Anthony's fire	Ergotism (and also erysipelas)
St Apollonia and St Avertin	Toothache
St Avidus	Deafness
St Benedict	Fever, kidney disease, and "temptations of the devil"
St Blasius	Quinsy
St Cathal	Herniae
St Catherine of Alexandria	Diseased tongues
St Clair	Conjunctivitis
St Drogo	Gravel in the urine
St Dymphna	Insanity
St Erasmus	Colic
St Fiacre	Haemorrhoids
St George	Syphilis
St Gervasius	Rheumatism
St Gete	Carcinoma
St Giles	Leprosy, lameness, insanity, and sterility
St Gotthard's tunnel disease	Ankylostomiasis
St Hilary of Poitiers	Backward children
St Hubert	Rabies
St Job	Syphilis
St Killian	Gout
St Lucy	Eye diseases, dysentery, and "haemorrhages in general"
St Main	Scabies
St Mathurin	Idiocy
St Matthias	Smallpox
St Modestus	Chorea
St Paul's evil	Epilepsy
St Roche	Plague
St Sement	Syphilis
St Valentine	Epilepsy
St Vitus' dance	Sydenham's chorea
St Winnoc	Whooping cough
St Zachary	Dumbness

19 October: Thomas Browne (1605-82)
Author of "Religio Medici" born and died

SHAKESPEARE ON SCROFULA
(OR THE KING'S EVIL)

...'Tis called the evil:
A most miraculous work in this good king,
Which often, since my here-remain in England,
I have seen him do. How he solicits heaven
Himself best knows; but strangely visited people,
All swol'n and ulcerous, pitiful to the eye,
The mere despair of surgery he cures;
Hanging a golden stamp about their necks
Put on with holy prayers; and 'tis spoken,
To the succeeding royalty he leaves
The healing benediction.

Macbeth (Act IV, Scene 3)

EUPHEMISMS: BREASTS

Amply endowed
    Boobies
        Bouncers
            Bristols
                Bubbies
                    Charms
                        Couple
                            Hemispheres
                                Hubba Bubbas
                            Jugs
                                  Knockers
                          Lungs
                      Mamas
                  Mamelles
                Mamms
              Maracas
            Mazoongas
        Orbs
      Tits
    Topless
Watermelons

---

24 October: Anton von Leeuwenhoek (1632-1723)
Invention of the microscope

INSECTS IN MEDICINE

Butterfly needle
Small needle used for temporary cannulation of vessels

Butterfly rash
Facial rash typical of systemic lupus erythematosus

Flea-bitten kidney
Multiple petechiae in infective endocarditis

Fly agaric (Amanita muscaria)
A type of hallucinogenic mushroom that contains muscarine, a cholinergic agonist

Muscae volitantes (flapping flies)
Floaters in the vitreous of the eye, appearing as specks in the line of sight

Spanish fly
Cantharides, an extract of the blister beetle, Lytta vesicatoria, used as an aphrodisiac, but which actually just causes penile irritation

Mosquito forceps

CELEBRITIES WITH HIP REPLACEMENTS

Maeve Binchy
Barbara Bush
George Bush Sr
Ray Charles
John Cleese
Reverend Billy Graham
Charlton Heston
Evel Knievel
Liza Minelli (twice)
Jack Nicklaus
Luciano Pavarotti
Dame Elizabeth Taylor
Eddie Van Halen
Murray Walker
Sir Jimmy Young

---

28 October: Jonas Edward Salk (1914-1995)
Development of polio vaccine

ANIMALS IN MEDICINE

Alopecia *(From the Greek word for fox; foxes had a form of mange causing baldness)*

Bats' wings sign *(Seen on a chest X-ray in pulmonary oedema)*

Bulldog forceps

Buphthalmos *(Seen in developmental glaucoma; Ox eye)*

Buffalo hump *(Physical sign seen in Cushing's disease)*

Cat's eye reflex *(White or yellowish retinal reflex in retinoblastoma)*

Cat eye syndrome *(Trisomy 22)*

Cauda equina *(Terminal nerve roots of the spinal cord; literally "horse's tail")*

Cheshire cat syndrome *(Failure to make a diagnosis because not all the signs and symptoms are present)*

Cri du chat syndrome *(Laryngeal abnormality leading to a cat-like cry in infants)*

Elephantiasis *(Obstructive lymphatic disease secondary to filarial worm infection)*

Hare lip *(Cleft lip)*

Leonine facies *(Seen in leprosy)*

LEOPARD syndrome *(**L**entigines, **E**CG abnormalities, **O**cular hypertelorism, **P**ulmonary stenosis, **A**bnormal genitalia, **R**etarded growth, **D**eafness)*

Lupus *(Any of several diseases, especially systemic lupus erythematosus, principally affecting the skin and joints; from the Mediaeval Latin for wolf)*

Monkey paw *(Chronic median nerve palsy causing typical hand posture in carpal tunnel syndrome)*

---

30 October: Gerhard Domagk (1895-1964)
Discovery of sulfonamides, Nobel prize 1939

ANIMALS IN MEDICINE (cont'd)

Ox heart *(Cor bovinum)*

Panda's eyes *(Physical sign in basal skull fractures)*

Raccoon's eyes *(Same sign as panda's eyes)*

Simian crease *(Politically incorrect term for the single palmar crease seen in conditions such as Down's syndrome and Cri du Chat Syndrome)*

MEDICALLY THEMED MOVIES

The Citadel (1938)
Doctor Jekyll and Mr Hyde (1941)
Doctor in the House (1954)
Doctor at Sea (1955)
Doctor at Large (1957)
Doctor in Distress (1963)
Dr Zhivago (1965)
Fantastic Voyage (1966)
M*A*S*H (1970)
The Hospital (1971)
One Flew Over the Cuckoo's Nest (1975)
Gross Anatomy (1989)
Awakenings (1990)
Vital Signs (1990)
Paper Mask (1990)
Flatliners (1990)
Doc Hollywood (1991)
The Doctor (1991)
Prince of Tides (1991)
City of Joy (1992)
Mr Jones (1993)
Outbreak (1995)
Critical Care (1997)
Patch Adams (1998)
Bringing Out The Dead (1999)

---

5 November: John Burdon Sanderson Haldane (1892-1964)
British geneticist, biologist, and popularizer of science

ETYMOLOGY: A-GO-GO

In Latin the suffix -ago, or -igo, or -ugo was often used to denote a disease (many of them diseases of the skin):

Albugo
A white opacification of the cornea

Caligo
Dim vision

Impetigo
A skin infection

Intertrigo
Inflammation of opposing skin at folds (e.g. under the breasts)

Lentigo
A freckle

Lumbago
Pain in the back

Porrigo
Dandruff

Prurigo
A chronic intensely itchy skin eruption

Serpigo
A creeping skin eruption, especially ringworm

Tentigo
Priapism or psychopathic lasciviousness

Vertigo
A form of dizziness in which the world seems to be spinning round the sufferer

Vitiligo
Depigmentation of patches of skin

---

7 November: Konrad Zacharias Lorenz (1903-1989)
Ethologist, Nobel prize for discoveries concerning organization of
individual and social behaviour pattern 1973

A SCIENTIFIC ALPHABET

Ciclosporin A
Amphotericin B
C virus (Coxsackie virus)
Actinomycin D
E for Ecstasy
Vitamin F (fatty acids e.g. linoleic acid)
Vitamin G (riboflavin)
Vitamin H (biotin)
I for an eye
Vitamin J (necessary for development in guinea pigs)
Vitamin K
Vitamin L
Vitamin M (folic acid)
O blood group
Vitamin P (flavouring factor in Hungarian red pepper and lemon juice)
Q fever (zoonosis caused by Coxiella burnetti)
Vitamin R (necessary for development of chickens)
Vitamin S (salicylate)
Vitamin T (fictitious vitamin named sesame seed factor; alternative name for testosterone)
Vitamin U (derivative of methionine which is also a fictitious vitamin)
Vitamin V (Viagra)
W (symbol for tryptophan)
Syndrome X
Y chromosome
Z for atomic number

ANATOMICALLY ENTITLED: BLOOD

The Colour of Blood
Novel by Brian Moore (1987), in which the discarding of the blood-coloured cardinal's robes is an important element

The Blood Doctor
Novel by Barbara Vine (2002) in which the main theme is hereditary disease, and in particular haemophilia

---

8 November: Christiaan Neethling Barnard (1922-2001)
First surgeon to perform a successful heart transplant

ILLNESSES AND DEATHS OF SOME US PRESIDENTS

George Washington (1789-1797)
Abscess left thigh ("malignant carbuncle") drained by Dr Samuel Bard; In 1799, purged, bled and blistered by Drs Craik, Dick and Brown for pneumonia/peritonsillar abscess but died

Andrew Jackson (1829-1837)
1806 and 1813 - shot in two separate duels

William Henry Harrison (4 March - 4 April 1841)
Purged and bled by his physician for pneumonia but died

Zachary Taylor (1849-1850)
1850 Died from severe diarrhoea ("cholera morbus") from food poisoning

Chester Alan Arthur (1881-1885)
1882 Bright's disease (a vague and obsolete term for acute and chronic diseases of the kidney)

Grover Cleveland (1885-1889, 1893-1897)
1893 excision of verrucous carcinoma of the hard palate and gingivae

Woodrow Wilson (1913-1921)
1919 stroke

Warren Gamaliel Harding (1921-1923)
Hypertensive heart disease

Franklin Delano Roosevelt (1933-1945)
1921 polio; 1944 hypertensive heart disease and bronchitis

Dwight David Eisenhower (1953-1961)
1955 heart attack; 1956 surgery for Crohn's disease; 1957 mild stroke

John Fitzgerald Kennedy (1961-1963)
1947 diagnosis of Addison's disease (progressive destruction of the adrenal gland with adrenocortical hormone deficiency; Jane Austen was thought to have suffered from it too)

---

13 November: Edward Adelbert Doisy (1893-1986)
Discovery of the chemical nature of vitamin K, Nobel prize 1943

ILLNESSES AND DEATHS OF
SOME US PRESIDENTS (cont'd)

Lyndon Baines Johnson (1963-1969)
1965 gallstone and gallbladder removal

Assassinated
Abraham Lincoln *(1865; John Wilkes Booth)*
James Abram Garfield *(1881; Charles J. Guiteau)*
William McKinley *(1901; Leon Czolgosz)*
John Fitzgerald Kennedy *(1963; ?Lee Harvey Oswald)*

THE GLADSTONE BAG

General practitioners often carry a Gladstone bag containing a wide variety of instruments, equipment and medications on home visits. Named after William Ewart Gladstone, the bag, made of stiff leather, consists of two hinged compartments. Sherlock Holmes refers to it in *The Man With The Twisted Lip*, "I have just been there and I have taken it out, and I have got it in this Gladstone bag," as does Dorian Gray to Basil Hallward in Oscar Wilde's novel *The Picture of Dorian Gray*, "What a way for a fashionable painter to travel! A Gladstone bag and an ulster!" Typical contents may include:

Torch
 Stethoscope
  Ophthalmoscope
   Patella hammer
    Peak flow meter
     Blood test tubes
      Blood glucose meter
       Sphygmomanometer
        Tongue depressor
         Gloves and lubricating jelly
          Emergency cardiac drugs (e.g. aspirin)
           Emergency allergy drugs (e.g. adrenaline)
            Emergency respiratory drugs (e.g. salbutamol)

---

14 November: Frederick Grant Banting (1891-1941)
Discovery of insulin

ANATOMICALLY ENTITLED: BRAIN

The Brain Eaters
Horror film directed by Bruno Vesota (1958)

Billion Dollar Brain
Film directed by Ken Russell (1967) starring Michael Caine,
the third in the Harry Palmer series, from the novel by Len Deighton (1966)

The Great Brain
Children's novel by John D Fitzgerald (1967)

The Man With Two Brains
Comedy film directed by Carl Reiner, starring Steve Martin and Kathleen
Turner (1983)

ANATOMICALLY ENTITLED: PENIS

Here Lies John Penis
A parody of Verlaine, by Geoffrey Count Montalk (1931). He was imprisoned in
Wormwood Scrubs for 6 months after having been convicted of obscenity (at
the trial he was supported by, amongst others, Virginia Woolf). After
imprisonment in Wormwood Scrubs, he became increasingly eccentric, dressing
in mock-mediaeval garb and laying claim to the throne of Poland

More Pricks Than Kicks
Short stories (1934) by Samuel Beckett, punning sexually on the Bible (Acts
9:5): "It is hard for thee to kick against the pricks"

Jake's Thing
A novel by Kingsley Amis (1978). Although Jake's "thing" is supposedly his
grudge against the world, it also implicitly refers to his penis

Prick Up Your Ears
A biography (1978), by John Lahr, of the homosexual playwright Joe Orton.
The play by Alan Bennett was filmed in 1987 by Stephen Frears, starring Gary
Oldman. Could the title be anagrammatic?

Puppetry of the Penis
A cabaret (1998), in which Simon Morley and David Friend twist their genitals
in a 50-minute show into objets d'art ("dick tricks" or genital origami)

---

15 November: Schack August Steenbergh Krogh (1874-1949)
Cardiovascular physiology, Nobel prize 1920

BREATHING PATTERNS

The normal pattern of breathing is quiet inspiration and expiration at a rate of about 12 times a minute, with an additional very deep breath every few minutes, in order to open up the furthest air passages, which have collapsed (atelectasis). However, sometimes the pattern changes:

Bouchut's respiration
Short inspiration followed by prolonged expiration, as in
children with a lung infection

Cheyne-Stokes respiration
Also called periodic respiration, in which breathing starts shallow and gets
deeper and deeper, stops for a few seconds, and then starts up again; this is
usually a sign that the brain stem is damaged, but it can occur in normal sleep

Cog-wheel respiration
In which there is jerky breathing

Corrigan's respiration
Shallow breathing, sometimes seen when there is a fever

Kussmaul respiration
Very deep breathing, as the body tries to get rid of carbon dioxide (e.g. when
there is too much acid in the body in severe diabetes)

Tachypnoea
Fast breathing (e.g. after exercise)

LITERARY DOCTORS: BRITISH

John Arbuthnot (1667-1735)
George Crabbe (1754-1832)
Michael Crichton (1942-)
A.J. Cronin (1896-1981)
Arthur Conan Doyle (1859-1930)
Oliver St John Gogarty (1878-1957)
Oliver Goldsmith (1728-1774)
W. Somerset Maugham (1874-1965)
Tobias Smollett (1721-1771)

18 November: George Wald (1906-1997)
Nobel prize for discoveries concerning the primary physiological
and chemical visual processes in the eye 1967

Coloured Diseases

Blackwater fever
Acute renal insufficiency with haemoglobinuria in malaria

Blue diaper syndrome
Tryptophan absorption syndrome

Brown tumours
Seen in hyperparathyroidism

Gray syndrome
Circulatory collapse in a child poisoned with chloramphenicol

Greenstick fractures
A type of fracture seen in children's bones

Pink disease
Acrodynia - mercury poisoning in children

Red man syndrome
Massive release of histamine due to rapid intravenous administration of vancomycin; histamine dilates blood vessels, making you turn red

Rose spots
Rose-coloured spots on the skin of the belly and loins in typhoid fever

Scarlet fever
Streptococcal sore throat and rash

Yellow fever
Mosquito-borne viral illness

Novels about Siamese twins

Leo and Theodore (1973) and *The Drunks* (1974)
(published as *Sweet Adversity* in 1978)   Donald Newlove
Brothers of the Head (1977)   Brian W. Aldiss
She and I (1991)   Eileen Lottman
Chang and Eng (2000)   Darin Strauss

---

19 November: George Emil Palade (1912-)
Internal composition of cells, Nobel prize 1974

HISTORICAL ALLUSIONS: MADNESS

Basket case
1919, American English, originally a literal reference to quadriplegic veterans of World War I; the figurative sense of "person emotionally unable to cope" is from 1967

Bedlam
1667, from colloquial pronunciation of the Hospital of Saint Mary of Bethlehem in London, founded 1247 as a priory and converted to a state lunatic asylum on dissolution of the monasteries in 1547

Mad as a hatter
1857, from erratic behaviour caused by prolonged exposure to the poison mercuric nitrate, used in making felt hats

EUPHEMISMS: ILLNESS AND INJURY

Afflicted
Blighty
Catch a packet
Combat ineffective
Cream crackered
Delicate
Dicky
Feel funny
Inconvenienced
Irish fever
Mayday
Misadventure
Mitotic disease
Off-colour
One foot in the grave
Poorly
Put out for the count
Scratch
So-so
Swing the lead
Winded
Winged

20 November: Karl von Frisch (1886-1982)
Ethologist, Nobel prize 1973

CURIOUS WORLD RECORDS

Longest attack of hiccups
Charles Osborne from Iowa in 1922 hiccupped 430 million times for a total of 60 years (his false teeth kept dropping out later on in life)

Longest sneezing fit
Donna Griffiths from Worcestershire started sneezing on 13th January 1931 and sneezed for 977 days (she sneezed a million times in the first year)

Highest measured snoring level
87.5 decibels - Melvyn Switzer of Hampshire (his wife is deaf in one ear)

Longest yawn
In 1888, a 50-year-old woman yawned continuously for 5 weeks

Longest fast
382 days by Angus Barbieri from Fife (his weight fell from 214 kg to 81 kg)

Most common non-contagious disease
Gum diseases such as gingivitis which affects 80% of the US population

Most common contagious disease
The common cold (acute coryza)

Most rare disease
Podocytoma of kidney (predicted by a Norwegian doctor but never described)

Most fatal disease
Kuru affects only the Fore tribe of Eastern New Guinea (who are cannibals) and is 100% fatal, but then so is life

Most rare fatal diseases in England and Wales
Yellow fever (last case in 1930)
Cholera (last case in 1938)
Bubonic plague (last case in 1936)

Most infectious disease
Pneumonic plague

---

22 November: Andrew Fielding Huxley (1917-)
Neurophysiology, Nobel prize for elucidating
ionic mechanisms in nerve cells 1963

Historical Allusions: People

Guillotine
1793, named after Joseph Guillotin (1738-1814), French physician, who as deputy to the National Assembly (1789) proposed, for humanitarian and efficiency reasons, that capital punishment be carried out by beheading on a machine, built in 1791 and first used in 1792.

Listerine
1879, American English, named after Joseph Lord Lister (1827-1912), English surgeon, who revolutionized modern surgery by applying Pasteur's discoveries and performing the first antiseptic surgery in 1865. Listerine was formulated by Dr Joseph Lawrence and Jordan Wheat Lambert as a multi-purpose disinfectant and marketed as an oral antiseptic by the Lambert Company in 1895. Lister objected in vain to the use of his name on the product.

Mesmerism
1802, from French mesmérisme, named for Franz Anton Mesmer (1734-1815), Austrian physician who developed a theory of animal magnetism and a mysterious body fluid, which allows one person to hypnotize another; the transfigurative sense of "enthral" is attested from 1862.

Munchausen syndrome
1850, in reference to Baron Karl Friedrich Hieronymus von Münchhausen (1720-97), a German adventurer who served in the Russian army against the Turks; his wildly exaggerated exploits can be found in the 1785 book "Baron Munchausen, Narrative of his Marvellous Travels" by Rudolph Erich Raspe (1734-94); as the syndrome of feigned illness, it is attested from 1951.

Nicotine
1819, named after Jean Nicot (c.1530-1600), French ambassador to Portugal, who sent tobacco seeds and powdered leaves back to France in 1561.

Pasteurize
To sterilize, for example milk, by heating. Named after the French bacteriologist Louis Pasteur (1822-1895), who first used the technique to stop fermentation in wine.

Schwannoma
A tumour of a nerve sheath, after Theodor Schwann (1810-1882).

---

27 November: Charles Scott Sherrington (1857-1952)
Discovery of neuronal functions, Nobel prize 1932

ANATOMICALLY ENTITLED: BONES

Bones of Contention
The title story in a book of short stories by Frank O'Connor (Michael Francis O'Donovan) (1936).

The Valley of Bones
Novel by Anthony Powell (1964), the seventh in the series entitled "A Dance to the Music of Time"; the title is from the Bible (Ezekiel 37:1): "The Hand of the Lord ... set me down in the midst of the valley which was full of bones".

What's Bred in the Bone
Novel by Robertson Davies (1985); the second volume in his "Cornish Trilogy".

The Bone People
Novel by Keri Hulme (1985), which won the Booker Prize that year, is about the management of an autistic child in New Zealand by musing on Maori culture; the "bone people" are the "beginning people" (i.e. the Maoris)

The Bone Collector
Film directed by Philip Noyce (1999) starring Denzel Washington as a quadriplegic homicide detective

PIECES OF POETRY: ABORTION

Fine Madam Would-be, wherefore should you fear,
That love to make so well, a child to bear?
The world reputes you barren: but I know
Your 'pothecary, and his drug says no.
Is it the pain affrights? That's soon forgot.
Or your complexion's loss? You have a pot,
That can restore that. Will it hurt your feature?
To make amends, you're thought a wholesome creature.
What should the cause be? Oh, you live at court:
And there's both loss of time and loss of sport
In a great belly. Write, then on thy womb,
Of the not born, yet buried, here's the tomb.

Ben Jonson,
Epigrams: LXII. To Fine Lady Would-be (1616)

---

29 November: Antonio Egas Moniz (1874-1955)
Discovery of leucotomy for psychoses, Nobel prize 1949

THE HIPPOCRATIC OATH

I swear by Apollo Physician and Asklepios and Hygieia and Panakeia and all the gods and goddesses, making them my witnesses, that I will fulfil according to my ability and judgment this oath and this covenant:

To hold him who has taught me this art as equal to my parents and to live my life in partnership with him, and if he is in need of money to give him a share of mine, and to regard his offspring as equal to my brothers in male lineage and to teach them this art - if they desire to learn it - without fee and covenant; to give a share of precepts and oral instruction and all the other learning to my sons and to the sons of him who has instructed me and to pupils who have signed the covenant and have taken an oath according to the medical law, but no one else.

I will apply dietetic measures for the benefit of the sick according to my ability and judgment; I will keep them from harm and injustice.

I will neither give a deadly drug to anybody who asked for it, nor will I make a suggestion to this effect. Similarly, I will not give to a woman an abortive remedy. In purity and holiness I will guard my life and my art.

I will not use the knife, not even on sufferers from stone, but will withdraw in favour of such men as are engaged in this work.

Whatever houses I may visit, I will come for the benefit of the sick, remaining free of all intentional injustice, of all mischief and in particular of sexual relations with both female and male persons, be they free or slaves.

What I may see or hear in the course of the treatment or even outside of the treatment in regard to the life of men, which on no account one must spread abroad, I will keep to myself, holding such things shameful to be spoken about.

If I fulfil this oath and do not violate it, may it be granted to me to enjoy life and art, being honoured with fame among all men for all time to come; if I transgress it and swear falsely, may the opposite of all this be my lot.

LEGENDS: MAIMONIDES

Also known by the nickname "Rambam", this Jewish physician, Moses ben Maimon, was born in Cordoba, Spain, in about 1135. He was a polymath and achieved fame as a physician, scholar, philosopher, and theologian. He translated Avicenna's Canon into Hebrew and wrote commentaries in Arabic on Galen, of whom he was critical, and Hippocrates. He became physician to the ruler Saladin and in 1187 wrote his Medical Aphorisms, which contained his writings on scientific method and rational medicine.

---

30 November: Edgar Douglas Adrian (1889-1977)
Discovery of the function of neurons, Nobel prize 1932

A FEW FICTIONAL PHYSICIANS

The Doctor of Physic
Geoffrey Chaucer, *The Canterbury Tales* (c. 1343-1400)

Doctor Charles Bovary
Gustav Flaubert, *Madame Bovary* (1856)

Doctor Thomas Thorne
Anthony Trollope, *Doctor Thorne* (1858)

Doctor Glas
Hjalmar Söderberg, *Doctor Glas* (1905)

Doctors Blenkinsop and Sir Colenso Ridgeon
George Bernard Shaw, *The Doctor's Dilemma* (1906)

Doctor Thorpe
William de Morgan, *Joseph Vance* (1906)

Doctor Thorndyke
Character in Richard Austin Freeman's series of novels and short stories, beginning with *The Red Thumb Mark* (1907); Freeman invented the detective story in reverse, in which the solution is given at the start of the book

Doctor John Dolittle
Hugh Lofting, *Doctor Dolittle* (1920)

Dr Aziz
E. M. Forster, *A Passage to India* (1924)

Doctor Julius No
Ian Fleming, *Doctor No* (1958)

Doc Daneeka
Joseph Heller, *Catch 22* (1961)

Doctor Stephen Maturin
The surgeon in Patrick O'Brian's series of naval books, beginning with *Master and Commander* (1970)

---

2 December: Joseph Bell (1837-1911)
Edinburgh physician, prototype for Sherlock Holmes

WORDS THAT DOCTORS MISSPELL

Since the abandonment of Greek and Latin as entrance requirements for medical schools, many UK doctors no longer understand the origins of the complicated words that they use every day. Consequently, they tend to misspell some of them. Listed below are some common examples. The figures in parentheses are the rates of errors per 10,000 correct instances in published papers listed in the biomedical database Pubmed. Since editors and copy-editors often correct errors in published papers before publication, these error rates are gross underestimates of the true frequencies in everyday practice. We would have written off the last three items in the list as printing typos had we not ourselves seen many examples of them in medical notes and manuscripts.

Wrong	Correct
Gentamycin (1030)	Gentamicin
Hydrocoele (406)	Hydrocele
Friedrich's ataxia (182)	Friedreich's ataxia
Malaena (111)	Melaena
Propanolol (106)	Propranolol
-paenia (72)	-penia[1]
Dipyramidole (21)	Dipyridamole
Withdrawl (9)	Withdrawal
Asprin (6)	Aspirin
Analgaesic (3)	Analgesic

[1]As in leukopenia, neutropenia, thrombocytopenia; the misspelling in this case is deliberate and arises from the mistaken idea that -penia is the American spelling of -paenia.

ANATOMICALLY ENTITLED: SKULLS

A Skull in Salop
A book of poems by Geoffrey Grigson (1967)

The Skull Beneath the Skin
Detective story by P D James (1982). The title is from T S Eliot:
"Webster was much possessed by death
And saw the skull beneath the skin"

2 December: George Richards Minot (1885-1950)
Discovery of liver therapy for pernicious anaemia, Nobel prize 1934

PLAGUES AND CONTAGION ON FILM

12 Monkeys (Terry Gilliam 1995; unknown virus)
28 Days Later (Danny Boyle, 2002; unknown virus)
The Andromeda Strain (Robert Wise, 1971; unknown virus)
Arrowsmith (John Ford, 1931; remade by Zdenek Zelenka, 1999;
unknown virus)
Bakterion (Tonino Ricci, 1976; unknown bacterium)
The Omega Man (Boris Sagal, 1971; unknown organism)
Outbreak (Wolfgang Petersen, 1995; Ebola virus)
Panic in the Streets (Elia Kazan, 1950; bubonic plague)
La Peste (Luis Puenzo, 1992; bubonic plague; from the
novel by Albert Camus)
The Satan Bug (John Sturges, 1965; unknown organism)

"TO BE OR NOT TO BE"

Literally hundreds of titles of papers in biomedical journals
quote Hamlet's famous question.
Here are those that were published in 2004 alone.

- *Bahnson TD, Grant AO. To be or not to be in normal sinus rhythm:
  what do we really know? Annals of Internal Medicine 2004;
  141: 727-9.*
- *Cengiz M. Internal mammary lymphatic irradiation: to be or not to be?
  Journal of Clinical Oncology 2004; 22: 2257-8.*
- *Doherty TM, Arditi M. TB, or not TB: that is the question - does TLR
  signalling hold the answer? Journal of Clinical Investigation 2004; 114:
  1699-703.*
- *Exley MA, Koziel MJ. To be or not to be NKT: natural killer T cells in
  the liver. Hepatology 2004; 40: 1033-40.*
- *Farooq A, Zhou MM. PTB or not to be: promiscuous, tolerant and
  Bizarro domains come of age. IUBMB Life 2004; 56: 547-57.*
- *Kucharczak J, Simmons MJ, Fan Y, Gelinas C. To be, or not to be: NF-
  kappaB is the answer - role of Rel/NF-kappaB in the regulation of
  apoptosis. Oncogene 2004; 23: 8858.*
- *Navarro-Vazquez A, Prall M, Schreiner PR. Cope reaction families: to
  be or not to be a biradical. Org Letters 2004; 6: 2981-4.*

4 December: Alfred Day Hershey (1908-1997)
Virus genetics, Nobel prize 1969

SHAKESPEARE ON POISONING

...whose effect
Holds such an enmity with blood of man
That swift as quicksilver it courses through
The natural gates and alleys of the body;
And with a sudden vigour it doth posset
And curd, like eager droppings into milk,
The thin and wholesome blood. So did it mine;...

"Murder most foul..." as spoken by the ghost
of Hamlet's father, *Hamlet* (Act I, Scene 5)

ALLOPATHIC ART

The Bradford frame
A traction device

Castellani's paint
A solution invented by Aldo Castellani (1877-1971) for treating skin infections

Modigliani syndrome
Pseudo-goitre

The Mona Lisa hypothesis
Most Obesities kNown Are Low In Sympathetic Activity

RENOIR
An expert computer system used to diagnose connective tissue disease and forms of arthritis (such as the painter Pierre-Auguste Renoir had)

Picasso
A procedure for deriving a minimal set of protein family profiles that cover all known protein sequences

PICASSO
The Paediatric Intensive Care Assessment of Outcome Study Group

The still life gene
A gene in Drosophila that encodes a protein homologous to guanine nucleotide exchange factors; also called sif

---

5 December: Carl Ferdinand Cori (1896-1984)
Discovery of the catalytic conversion of glycogen, Nobel prize 1947

DON'TS FOR DIAGNOSTICIANS

Don't be too clever
Don't diagnose rarities
Don't be in a hurry
Don't be faddy
Don't mistake a label for a diagnosis
Don't diagnose two diseases simultaneously in the same patient
Don't be too cock-sure
Don't be biased
Don't hesitate to revise your diagnosis from time to time in a chronic case

By Sir Robert Hutchison,
The Principles of Diagnosis, *British Medical Journal* (1928) volume 28, pages
335-7, reproduced with permission from the BMJ publishing group.

MEDICAL GEOMETRY: TRIANGLES

Einthoven's triangle
An imaginary equilateral triangle with the heart at its centre, its sides representing the three standard limb leads of the electrocardiogram.

Black triangle

This symbol, which marks certain drugs in the British National Formulary, reminds doctors to report adverse effects of those drugs to the regulatory authorities in the UK

Bochdalek's triangle
A triangular slit in the diaphragm

Earle's triangle
The avulsed posterior edge of the tibia in fracture-dislocations of the ankle

Volkmann's triangle
Earle's triangle misattributed

The anterior and posterior triangles of the neck
There are five anatomical areas in the neck that are triangular, three anteriorly (the superior carotid, inferior carotid, and submandibular triangles) and two posteriorly (the occipital and subclavian triangles)

---

10 December: Howard Martin Temin (1934-1994)
Discovery of viral reverse transcriptase, Nobel prize 1975

BEDSIDE LIBRARY FOR MEDICAL STUDENTS (OUR RECOMMENDATIONS)

Non-fiction (*see also* Autopathography)

- The DNA Trilogy:
  The Double Helix by James D Watson (1968).
  What Mad Pursuit by Francis Crick (1988) (The title is from Keats's poem *Ode to a Grecian Urn*).
  The Third Man of the Double Helix by Maurice Wilkins (2003).
  Three strongly contrasting autobiographies from the three men who won the Nobel prize for discovering the structure of DNA. Brenda Maddox's biography of Rosalind Franklin, *The Dark Lady of DNA* (2002), is also worth reading.
- *Talking Sense* by Richard Asher (1972). Medical wisdom from an experienced physician.
- *Gödel, Escher, Bach* by Douglas Hofstadter (1979). How music, art, and mathematics collide with DNA and what artificial intelligence has to do with it.
- *Science Good, Bad and Bogus* by Martin Gardner (1981). Anything by Gardner is worth reading. This one teaches you to be sceptical.
- *Surely You're Joking, Mr Feynman!* by Richard P Feynman (1985). The rumbustious memoirs of an unusual Nobel prize-winning physicist, safe-breaker, artist, and bongo drum player.
- *The Man Who Mistook His Wife for a Hat* by Oliver Sacks (1985). A fascinating collection of neurological case histories. The title story was made into a chamber opera by Michael Nyman (1986).
- *The Penguin Book of Curious and Interesting Puzzles* by David Wells (1992). Good exercises for the mind, to train you to get through those silly interviews with off-the-wall questions.
- *The Greatest Benefit to Mankind* by Roy Porter (1997). The best short(ish) history of medicine "from antiquity to the present".
- *The Mould in Doctor Florey's Coat* by Eric Lax (2004). How penicillin was isolated in Oxford by Florey, Chain, and Heatley.
- *Hippocratic Oaths* by Raymond Tallis (2004). A superb account of the malaise of modern medicine.
- *The Medical Miscellany* by Manoj Ramachandran and Max Ronson (2005). Riveting collection of curious & interesting medical facts.

---

11 December: Robert Koch (1843-1910)
German bacteriologist, Nobel prize for discoveries and inventions related to tuberculosis 1905

ARTHROPODS IN MEDICINE

Cancer and carcinoma
Cancer is Latin for a crab and karkinos Greek

Hans Krebs
The surname of the Nobel prize-winning biochemist Hans Krebs, who described the citric acid cycle, named after him, means crab (and cancer) in German

Arachnodactyly
Long spidery fingers; seen in conditions such as Marfan's syndrome

Arachnoiditis
Inflammation of the arachnoid membrane that surrounds the brain

Spider naevus/angioma
An abnormal cutaneous collection of blood vessels; increased numbers can be seen in chronic liver disease, pregnancy, and hyperthyroidism

Subarachnoid haemorrhage
Haemorrhage into the subarachnoid space, between the arachnoid mater and pia mater, membranes that surround the brain

AN UNUSUAL JOB ADVERTISEMENT

Global executive seeks MD to serve as personal physician.
Responsible for round-the-clock medical care.
Supervises Medical Unit staff of approximately 16 military personnel.
Provides medical care to Executive's family, Second-In-Command, Cabinet members and Executive Branch Employees.
Private office on ground floor of residence.
Additional treatment facilities in nearby Executive Office Building.
Ideal candidate will be able to successfully interact with government bureaucracy, reporters, and politicians.
Confidentiality regarding employer's business and personal activities a must.
Extensive international travel required.
Salary commensurate with experience and/or military rank.
Send resume and reference to President of the United States,
The White House, Washington, DC.

---

12 December: Erasmus Darwin (1731-1802)
English physician, grandfather of Charles Darwin

DEAF MUSICIANS

Ludwig van Beethoven (1770-1827)
Beethoven started to become deaf at about the age of 30 and wrote the famous Heiligenstadt Testament (1802), in which he came to terms with the inevitability of his growing deafness and described his consequent despair.

Bedrich Smetana (1824-1884)
Smetana went rapidly and completely deaf in 1874. In the final movement of his first string quartet in E minor ("From My Life", 1876) a lively dance is interrupted abruptly by a protracted high-pitched E, symbolizing his tinnitus.

Robert Franz (1815-1892)
Franz became increasingly deaf from about the age of 26, but continued to compose songs until forced to stop in 1868.

Gabriel Fauré (1845-1924)
Deafness became an increasingly serious handicap for Fauré from about the age of 55, until it forced him to resign the Directorship of the Paris Conservatoire in 1920. However, he continued to compose, producing such works as the second piano quintet, the string trio, and the string quartet.

Other deaf musicians
Shawn Dale Barnett, drummer   Evelyn Glennie, percussionist
Fujiko Hemming, pianist   Pete Townshend, rock musician
Def Leppard

SUICIDE IN OPERA:
JUMPING FROM A HEIGHT

La muette di Portici (Daniel-François-Esprit Auber, 1828)
Fenella, the mute dancer, jumps into the sea from the castle when she learns that her brother Masaniello has been killed.

Le Roi d'Ys (Edouard Lalo, 1888)
Margared, daughter of the King of Ys, jumps from a precipice in expiation for the crime of helping an enemy open the floodgates that protect her city from the sea.

---

13 December: George Davis Snell (1903-1996)
Genetic determination of immune responses, Nobel prize 1908

CLASSICS: DE MATERIA MEDICA

Pedanius Dioscorides probably lived between 40 AD and 90 AD in the time of the Roman Emperors Nero and Vespasian. A learned physician, he practised medicine as an army doctor, and saw service with the Roman legions in Greece, Italy, Asia Minor, and Provence in modern-day France. His military years provided opportunities for studying diseases, collecting and identifying medicinal plants, and discovering other healing materials. Dioscorides compiled his medical treatise at the suggestion of a fellow-physician, Areius. He had access to the library at Alexandria and may have studied at Tarsus.

Dioscorides probably wrote his great herbal in about 64 AD (according to Pritzel 77 AD). In *Materia Medica* (five volumes), he described the medicinal properties of about six hundred plants and nearly one thousand drugs. This book remained the standard pharmacy textbook until the 17th century.

"MORE EQUAL THAN OTHERS"

Did George Orwell know how popular this phrase would become when he coined it in Animal Farm (1945)? Here are some examples of its use in medical publications.

- *Jacobs BS, Carhuapoma JR, Castellanos M. Clarifying TCD criteria for brain death - are some arteries more equal than others? Journal of Neurological Science 2003; 210: 3-4.*
- *Levi M. All heparins are equal, but some are more equal than others. Journal of Thrombosis and Haemostasis 2003; 1: 884-5.*
- *Paterson A. All alleles are equal, but some alleles are more equal than others. Molecular Psychiatry 1998; 3: 212.*
- *Probyn AJ. Some drugs more equal than others: pseudo-generics and commercial practice. Australian Health Review 2004; 28: 207-17.*

But only two titles mention animals, as in Orwell's original:
- *Raible F, Arendt D. Metazoan evolution: some animals are more equal than others. Current Biology 2004; 14: R106-8.*
- *Williams G, Patrick AW. Are some animals more equal than others? Diabetic Medicine 1992; 9: 215-17.*

15 December: Maurice Hugh Frederick Wilkins (1916-2004)
Discovery of the structure of DNA, Nobel prize 1962

Movies Called "Virus"

Apocalypse Domani (aka "Virus"; Antonio Margheriti, 1980; virus)
Fukkatsu no hi (aka "Virus"; Kinji Fukasaku, 1980; virus)
Virus (aka "Cannibal Virus"; Bruno Mattei, 1980; zombies)
Virus (aka "Robin Cook's Virus"; Armand Mastroianni, 1995; Ebola virus)
Spill (aka "Virus"; Allan A Goldstein, 1996; virus)
Contagious (aka "Virus"; Joe Napolitano, 1997; cholera)
Virus (John Bruno, 1999; electronic alien life form)
Virus (Marko Sopic, 2001; virus)
Virus (Rusty Nelson, 2002; computer virus)
Virus (Francesco Campanini, 2003; cancer)

Sea Creatures in Medicine

Anchovy sauce
Amoebic abscess

Carcinoma
Cancer (meaning crab)

Fishhook sign
Upward curving ureters on X-ray due to an enlarged prostate gland

Hippocampus
A part of the brain, shaped like a "seahorse"

Ichthyosis
Disease of the skin resembling fish scales (Greek ichthus meaning fish)

Phocomelia
Seen in congenital malformations, e.g. due to thalidomide; phocos meaning seal and melia meaning limb, thus "seal flippers"

Salmon patch
Salmon coloured spot on the cornea as evidence of syphilis (Salmonella is named after Daniel Elmer Salmon (1850-1914), not the fish)

Shark skin
Riboflavin deficiency

---

21 December: Hermann Joseph Muller (1890-1967)
Discovery of mutational effects of X-rays, Nobel prize 1946

THE FOUR HUMORS

The humoral theory, which had its inception in ancient Greek thought, was the fundamental basis of explanations of health and disease based on the scientific thoughts of, amongst others, the PreSocratics and Pythagoreans. The earliest formulation of humoralism can be found in the Hippocratic treatise *On the Nature of Man*. When the four humors, which were blood, yellow bile, black bile, and phlegm, were in balance in the body, good health followed. Disease was thought to be a result of an imbalance of one or more of these humors. The humors were paired with specific seasons of the year, which represented specific qualities. They were also paired with the four elements first described by Empedocles, of which all things were composed, earth, air, fire, and water. Here is a diagrammatic representation of the humoral theory:

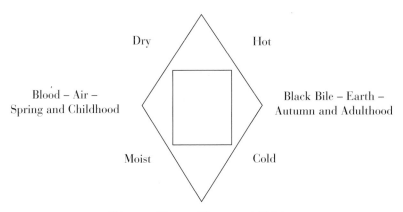

Yellow Bile – Fire – Summer and Youth

Dry

Hot

Blood – Air –
Spring and Childhood

Black Bile – Earth –
Autumn and Adulthood

Moist

Cold

Phlegm – Water – Winter and Old Age

The four humours are also associated with different states of mind:

- Blood = sanguine (hopeful; Latin sanguis = blood)
- Yellow bile = choleric (irascible; Greek chole = bile)
- Black bile = melancholic (depressed; Greek melas = black)
- Phlegm = phlegmatic (unemotional; Greek phlegma = inflammation)

22 December: Halden Keffer Hartline (1903-1983)
Processing of light by the retina, Nobel prize 1967

EUPHEMISMS: THE END

Acres
  After parts
    Backside
      Back garden
        Back passage
          Basement
            Behind
              Bender
                Bottle
                  Bottom
                    Bronze eye
                      Buns
                        Butt
                          Can
                            Cheeks
                              Derrière
                                Elephant and castle
                                  Exhaust pipe
                                    Heinie
                                      Honkles
                                        Ireland
                                          Kelster
                                        Khyber
                                      Kingdom
                                    Latter end
                                  Posterior
                                Rear
                              Ring
                            Rump
                          Seat
                        Second eye
                      Sit-me-down
                    Sit-upon
                  Stern
                Sunday face
              Tail
            Tochus
          Tush

27 December: Louis Pasteur (1843-1910)
Pioneering French microbiologist

COLLECTED CONTENTS

MISCELLANEOUS SUGGESTIONS

Almost certainly there will be an item that you think should have been included in the *Medical Miscellany* but is not here. Please use this page to write to us, letting us know about it so that we can include it in future editions. (N.B. If it is a direct quotation we need to know exact details of the original publication in order to clear copyright.)

Hammersmith Press Ltd
496 Fulham Palace Road
London
SW6 6JD

OTHER HAMMERSMITH PRESS PUBLICATIONS

Chronic Fatigue Syndrome – a natural way to treat M.E.
By Professor Basant K. Puri

160 pp   £14.99
ISBN: 1-905140-002

In this ground-breaking new book Professor Puri brings together historical and contemporary evidence to show how M.E. is almost certainly a physical, or 'organic', condition resulting from viral and other influences that reduce essential chemicals in the body. As such it can be treated, and in a natural cost-effective way. Read how and why EPA ('eicosapentaenoic acid') will be essential to recovery, how to take it, what supplements to have with it, and how to change to a lifestyle that will promote recovery. Read also why DHA ('deoxyribonucleic acid') should be avoided in supplement form.

'Professor Puri writes very well. He explains scientific ideas in a way that makes it possible for the general reader to understand and includes interesting asides and personal comments. It is such a relief to be able to read that a consultant in one of our local hospitals thinks M.E. is a real physical disease.'

Catriona Courtier, Editor of *OutReach*

Attention Deficit Hyperactivity Disorder – a natural way to treat ADHD
By Professor Basant K. Puri

192pp   £14.99
ISBN: 1-905140-01-0
Due for publication: July 2005

A fresh look at ADHD, the controversial condition that is being increasingly diagnosed in children in the developed world and treated with powerful drugs. Professor Basant Puri examines the underlying metabolic problems and dietary imbalances that may lie behind hyperactive behaviour, and the ways in which these deficiencies can be addressed. Parents and carers of children with ADHD will find new hope in combating this relentless condition.

October 2005
Guide to Traditional Medicines
By Dr Lakshman Karalliedde

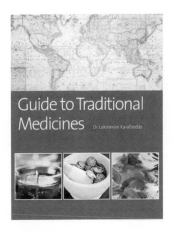

240pp   £15.99
ISBN: 1-905140-04-5
Due for publication: October 2005

A highly structured compendium, bringing together what is currently known and has been scientifically validated regarding traditional medicines from around the world. Bringing together Chinese, Afro-Caribbean, Unani and Ayurvedic traditional medicines, this book covers the sources of these medicines, their known effects and side-effects, recommended dosages, and precautions.

ABOUT HAMMERSMITH PRESS LTD

An independent publisher providing books on matters relating to diet, health and illness for the non-specialist reader.

Hammersmith Press is a new publishing house producing books for the general public and health professionals that promote better health and well being through a greater understanding of diet, nutrition and the functioning of the human body and mind.

Founded in 2004 we see a need for books that address readers as interested, intelligent custodians of their own health and who want to have thorough explanations of the advice they are given rather than taking guidance on trust.

While this is a very serious remit, we believe there are definite health benefits in not being serious all the time...